BETWEEN STARS AND ATOMS

Albert Einstein (1879–1955). One of the most important
founders of modern science, of whom it was rightly said
by the Dutchman, Prof. E. W. Beth: 'Large sections of
present-day science and contemporary techniques would
be inconceivable without the contributions of Einstein.'

Between Stars and Atoms

A PRESENT-DAY JOURNEY THROUGH
THE WORLD AND SPACE

Eibert H. Bunte

TRANSLATED BY IAN F. FINLAY

London
MICHAEL JOSEPH

First published in Holland by
AD. M.C. Stok, The Hague
in 1961 under the title
DE MENS TUSSEN GROOT EN KLEIN

This translation first published by
MICHAEL JOSEPH LTD
26 Bloomsbury Street
London, W.C.1
1962

Set and printed in Great Britain by Unwin Brothers Limited at the Gresham
Press, Woking, in Plantin type, eleven point, leaded, on paper made by Henry
Bruce at Currie, Midlothian, and bound by James Burn at Esher

'It is most important that the public as a whole should have the opportunity to follow the methods and results of scientific research consciously and with proper understanding. It is not sufficient that each new discovery should be adopted, developed and applied by a few specialists only. The limiting of all scientific knowledge to a small group kills the philosophical interest of a nation and leads to intellectual poverty.'

ALBERT EINSTEIN

PREFACE

A word of explanation

On the one hand a rocket to the moon, on the other a nuclear reactor; on the one hand a star, on the other an atom; on the one hand the macrocosm, on the other the microcosm—and man in between. That is what this book is about.

Man is about half-way between the one extreme and the other. Based on the amount of matter, about as many people would be needed to construct one average star as there are atoms in the human body.

Man stands between what is large and what is small, and his interest and desire for knowledge extend equally to both. He photographs the far side of the moon and splits uranium atoms. As little as a quarter of a century ago, these achievements would have been considered completely impossible. Close co-operation between scholars and technicians will during the next twenty-five years lead to results of which no one dares as yet to dream.

Man will be confronted in his material, but particularly also in his spiritual life to an ever-increasing extent with the results of scientific research. Not only the nuclear physicist and the astronomer, the reactor technician and the builder of rockets will have to familiarize themselves with the large amount of new material in order to be able to work with these new discoveries, but the baker and business man, the accountant and shorthand typist will also have to try to gain some understanding of what is new, in order to be able to live with it.

This book is written for the baker, the business man, the accountant and the shorthand typist. It does not contain anything new—the expert and the already interested layman can leave it unread without any scruples. They, however, form a small minority. Most people will need this book. The baker finds all the fuss about Luniks and Explorers strange. The shorthand typist is basically afraid of those weird nuclear reactors. The business man has merely heard of Einstein, and would really like to know what that man did in fact invent. And the accountant is concerned by what is after all meant by radioactivity. They will all find the beginning of an answer in this book.

The beginning of an answer, nothing more. For many, this will be sufficient to form an approximate picture of what is being taught on all manner of points by modern science and what it is striving for. Others will take up another book after this one, in which they will find a fuller account of various subjects.

This book is, therefore, definitely not a text-book; on the other hand, it is just as definitely not 'science fiction'—this is stressed in order to avoid any misunderstanding.

This book is a 'translation'; the most important facts and suppositions concerning modern science, contained in innumerable books and other writings in technical language and formulae, are here translated into simple words comprehensible to everyone. The author has here and there been confronted with the difficult choice as to whether to sacrifice simplicity for the sake of accuracy, or to be somewhat less strict as regards accuracy in order to preserve simplicity. There are, after all, scientific subjects which cannot be explained exactly in simple terms. In general, he has preferred to lay greater stress on simplicity, without however ever positively violating the truth. A picture which is perhaps not quite correct in minor details is better than one which is, as a whole, unintelligible, provided the total impression on the non-expert observer is correct.

The reader will not be bored with long series of dry figures or be deterred by mathematical formulae. These cannot, however, be neglected entirely. For the benefit of 'connoisseurs,' the author has added an appendix containing the most important figures, formulae and calculations discussed in the book.

It is hoped that this book will find its way to the readers for whom it has been written: the baker and the business man, the accountant and the shorthand typist, and to all the thousands of others for whom science is still a closed book, and who look around with increasing astonishment in a society on which science will make an ever stronger impression. It is hoped that it will assist them in acquiring the beginning of an understanding of man's place between the macrocosm and the microcosm.

EIBERT H. BUNTE

CONTENTS

ILLUSTRATIONS

CHAPTER I

A REVOLUTION IN CLASSICAL SCIENCE. LIGHT AND GRAVITY.
BECQUEREL DISCOVERS RADIOACTIVITY. DEMOLISHERS
TURNED OUT TO BE BUILDERS

The man took the photographic plate carefully out of the developer. He held the wet glass up to the weak red light, just for a moment, since the plate had still to be fixed. He smiled contentedly for there was a black spot on the negative at the place where the uranium crystal had been lying. Just as he had expected, the crystal had shown fluorescent properties after it had been lying in the sun for a short time. It had then radiated the sunlight it had absorbed, exposing the plate in this way.

The man was, however, not completely satisfied—certain things were not right. The sulphides of calcium and zinc behaved differently. He took a new plate, wrapped it up so that the light could not get to it, and fixed the uranium crystal on it. He now placed a small metal plate, shaped in the form of a cross, between the plate and the crystal. He would now lay this in the sun and see what happened. He opened the shutters of the laboratory windows. There was no sun, but fog. In the winter twilight the streets were filled with grey smoke. Could it be as late as that?

Then I won't bother, he thought, and pushed the plate with the crystal and cross into a drawer. This test was, after all, not that important and other work was waiting to be done.

A few weeks later when he was sitting rummaging in his desk, he found the contraption again. And without really knowing why, he decided to develop the plate. There could, of course, not be anything on it, since the crystal had not been lying in the sun and could therefore not have absorbed any energy to emit a radiation. He looked at the developed negative in the red light of the darkened room. He frowned. There was a dark spot on the plate on which the form of a cross stood out as white.

The man stood for a long time with the moist plate in his hand, thinking deeply. The plate had been exposed, the radiation had not been brought about by him. Uranium must then emit a radiation completely of its own accord, without external influences. Strange. Surely it must be the same type of radiation as his colleague Röntgen had discovered a short time ago in Germany. It would have to be investigated more closely.

Carefully, the man fixed the strange plate. It was Sunday, 2nd February, 1896. Antoine Henri Becquerel, Professor at a French University, had discovered radioactivity.

On this particular Sunday a further blow had been struck at the foundations of the structure of classical science, a structure which had been erected stone by stone during centuries of hard work on the part of generations of scholars. It was a proud structure, with such solid foundations and its bricks set so firmly, that it would stand up, without difficulty, to future centuries. It still had a few imperfections, but what has not? They would be remedied by study and experimenting.

But those few imperfections seemed to be the cause of what nobody would ever have dared to predict in the 'eighties of the last century, namely a revolution in science which caused the proud structure to rock so violently that its collapse seemed near at hand. The foundations had turned out to be unsound. There would have to be a lot of demolition.

One of those responsible for this was Professor Becquerel, not that it was his wish to be, for he was not a revolutionary. It was also nothing but pure chance that he was the man who discovered radioactivity. If he had not developed that second plate, the natural radiation of uranium would not have been discovered on that particular day in February 1896, but on another day during the last few years of the nineteenth century or at the beginning of this one. It would, nevertheless, have been discovered. Discoveries are made when the time is ripe, just as a thunder-storm breaks loose when the atmosphere has become too strongly loaded with electricity—nobody can do anything about it. It has often happened in the history of science that two people have made the same discovery at the same time, independently of one another and even without knowing one another.

The wet plate in Becquerel's hands was one of the proofs that

14

nature did not behave at all in the way in which scholars had worked out in minute detail, and within a few decades numerous other discoveries followed which confirmed this again and again. The perfection of classical science was an illusion.

Becquerel was one of the men who undermined the foundations of classical science. Others included Madame Curie, Planck, Einstein, Rutherford and Bohr. It was due to them that the foundations were so severely affected that the demolition of a section of the structure seemed necessary. It was also due to them that new foundations were laid, making possible a sound restoration of the structure of science, a restoration which at the same time involved a radical modernization. As a result, the structure has become more serviceable and habitable. Science does not merely demolish, it also constructs, and this is its main activity. Madame Curie, Planck, Einstein, Rutherford, Bohr and all the others were primarily builders.

Man now lives in the new scientific structure erected by them. The building is not yet finished, and will probably never be completed. Perhaps this is one reason why outsiders who come to visit the building cannot find their way about. It all creates such a confusing impression. The visitor wanders round like a helpless blind man. He does not understand anything about what he touches and he does not understand the language which is spoken there. Yet synchrocyclotrons and nuclear reactors, electronic calculating machines and artificial satellites, rockets and radioactive isotopes, radio telescopes and electron microscopes, as well as atomic and hydrogen bombs come out of that building.

The average outsider does not know anything about modern science, although it has a great influence on his life, an influence which will continue to grow in the years to come. This gives him a feeling of discomfort—he likes to know what he is dealing with.

Naturally not every layman can go and study science in order to find out what is happening around him, but he can certainly allow himself to be led by a guide. He can be shown the ground-plan of the scientific structure by that guide, he can have explained to him what this and that are used for, and he can have the most important expressions in a language which is foreign to him explained in words he understands. Then at least he will be able to form a reasonable judgment concerning what is new and which can influence his life to such an extent. He will no longer be confused so quickly.

More is not necessary. One does not need to know the theory of electricity in order to switch on a light, nor does one need to know how the works fit together in order to be able to look at a clock.

This book will try to be such a guide. It will try to describe the position in modern science in broad outline and to show that everything fits together, from an artificial satellite to a nuclear reactor, from the Milky Way to atomic nuclei. It is the great merit of modern scientists that they have together drawn up a coherent picture of the world. Their work is like the putting together of the individual pieces of a jig-saw puzzle, the picture becoming clearer as more pieces are put in place. The jig-saw puzzle of 'nature' will, however, never be finished, because the number of pieces is infinitely large. This is realized to an increasing extent in scientific circles as people advance along the capricious paths leading to the ultimate goal. The present servants of science are in this respect very different from their predecessors at the end of the nineteenth century.

Those predecessors thought they had done a great deal, and that in a short time science would be complete. The revolution of which Professor Becquerel was unwittingly one of the originators nevertheless brought about a basic change in this manner of thinking.

Many scientists did not want to accept this revolution, but it was more powerful than they were, more powerful than the firmly established facts which had been passed down from generation to generation. Scientists have been forced to accept that nothing is established once and for all.

This must, in fact, have been difficult for many of them, for things were really very secure as far as science was concerned in the second half of the preceding century. The whole of nature was a well-lubricated machine which ran perfectly, and scholars had gradually gained a full understanding of the working of that machine. Everything could be calculated, and the result was always correct. Eclipses of the sun and moon could be predicted accurately to the very second. The existence of radio waves had to be accepted on theoretical grounds, and behold—they did in fact exist and obeyed the theory precisely. The chemical elements no longer formed a disorderly collection, but had been arranged nicely in a safe in which each had its own place, resulting in the Periodic System, so that their behaviour no longer caused any surprises. The planets followed orbits around the sun, and these could be calculated so exactly that even an as yet unknown planet could be tracked down with nothing more than pencil and paper, and turned out to be where the calculation indicated that it should be.

Yes, scientists had certainly placed their house nicely in order. They could calculate and explain everything, and there could be no surprises. Would it not appear from all this that the foundations of their theory were absolutely correct?

A few details still had to be investigated more closely and explained. There was light, for example. Science taught that light is an electromagnetic vibration or wave motion. It reaches us from the sun as well as from other sources, but—and here was the problem—it passes through empty space on the way. How can a wave motion be propagated through empty space? A wave motion presupposes something that can vibrate. There are the waves on the sea which represent a movement of the water. Sound waves involve a movement of the air. In an empty space there is, however, nothing that can move—and yet light is propagated. Scholars solved the difficulty by assuming the existence of a substance which was said to fill the whole universe uniformly, a substance to which they gave the name ether. This ether vibrated and consequently light could pass through space. It was now merely a question of proving the presence of ether experimentally. Once that was done, this problem too would be solved according to the classical laws.

Another unexplained difficulty concerned gravity, the force which causes the planets to follow their orbits around the sun and which causes a stone which has been thrown up into the air to fall back to the ground. One of the strange things about this force was that it acted immediately, that is to say without requiring any time during which to propagate itself. It was known that light has a finite speed of something less than 300,000 kilometres a second and needs time to travel from the sun to the earth for example. The force of gravity, however, worked immediately—what could it be exactly? It must in any case have different properties from all other types of force.

Would there also be no agreement at all, at least in some respects, between the force of gravity and electromagnetic phenomena? Would nature be hermaphroditic?

These then were some of the problems. And there were also the new types of radiation of Röntgen and Becquerel. Well, once the answer had been found, science would be virtually complete. The flag could then be flown at full-mast.

The answer was found—and it set loose the revolution. In general, science seemed fit for use in the house, garden and kitchen, but it failed completely in explaining the last difficulties. Its foundations were unsound.

The question of ether was decided by an historical experiment by the American scientist, A. A. Michelson. He had designed an apparatus for seeking out the ether. If this mysterious substance existed, then the apparatus would positively show it. When Michelson carried out his experiment, in Chicago in 1887, all the trams in the city were stopped in order to avoid even the slightest disturbance. An unambiguous question was put to nature—yes or no—and the answer was no.

The ether appeared not to exist—and subsequently it also appeared to be quite unnecessary that it should. Light certainly behaves as a wave, but also as a stream of material particles. It turned out not to be an uninterrupted stream of energy, but was nicely apportioned into extremely small units called quanta, and these quanta could propagate themselves in empty space just as matter can also move through it. In short, energy and matter appeared to have much in common. In the end, they even turned out to be identical!

And what of the force of gravity? It was not a problem at all—it turned out not to exist as a force. The phenomenon of the force of gravity appeared to be a result of what has come to be known as the curvature of space.

Radiation defied all the rules. The elements did not seem to be bothered about the Periodic System after all. Certain of them changed of their own accord into other elements and skipped from one compartment to the other. Radium, for example, the new element discovered by Madame Curie, appeared to emit rays, consisting amongst other things of nuclei of helium atoms, and to pass via all sorts of intermediate stages into lead.

The bases of classical science passed away. Nature was not after all a machine whose working could be described completely and exactly. What was it then?

Scientists calculated and experimented. They propounded theories and rejected them, changed them, accepted them. New science soon acquired shape. Young scholars conquered the field by storm under the command of a young examiner in the Patent Office in Berne, a certain Albert Einstein. They measured and calculated, started from brand-new suppositions, and experimented. And behold, everything now seemed to fit together much better. All the old things which had remained intact in science could easily be explained in the new way, and what was formerly obscure could now also be explained. It was, after all, possible to explain the workings of nature, except for the smallest details. A fraction of uncertainty remained everywhere, but that did not matter since the system as a whole worked well. It was paradoxical, for in spite of the lack of an absolutely firm foundation, the modernized scientific structure acquired firmer and stronger foundations than ever, although no one dares to say that the last word has now been said on this point.

This all happened in a few decades. The consequences of all manner of discoveries were enormous, for man learnt a trick from nature and even succeeded in changing atoms. He thereby broke open a treasure-house crammed full with new energy. He succeeded in clearing up numerous secrets in the unfathomable depths of the universe by means of his new knowledge and in viewing the relationship between the elements of nature with new eyes.

We are now going to survey all the things that man has learned. The following chapters will show what science knows at the moment—or considers it knows—about the earth, the sky, the universe, materials, atoms, energy, time and space. Starting from the familiar earth, we shall visit the moon, the sun, the planets, the stars, the Milky Way and the milliards of other solar systems. We shall pass through time and space and descend into the extremely small world of atoms. We shall look at nuclear reactors and cyclotrons, we shall analyse atoms and find out what radioactivity is.

Finally, we shall attempt to introduce some order into the

great synthesis which appears to exist between the extremely large and the extremely small, and to say something about the ultimate harmony which resounds in all creation, a harmony which we, on our enormous, and yet so minute globe, do not succeed in achieving.

CHAPTER II

THE EARTH AND THE MOON—MOTHER AND CHILD OR
DOUBLE PLANET? COPERNICUS WAS RIGHT. FROM GALILEO
GALILEI TO WERNHER VON BRAUN. A LIFELESS MASS OF
STONE

A half-blind old man stepped into the hall of the Santa Maria
sopra Minerva monastery in Rome to face the stern judges of the
Holy Inquisition. He was the sixty-nine year old Italian
mathematician and scientist Galileo Galilei, once Professor at
Padua and court mathematician to the Grand Duke of Tuscany.
Trembling, he raised his right hand and stammering took the
oath, being prompted by the president of the court. The
judges listened, unmoved. Galileo swore that the earth was the
fixed and immutable centre of the universe. He renounced the
heretical theories of the Polish–German astronomer Nicolaus
Copernicus which had been condemned by the Church and
placed on the Index.

In order to save himself, the old man renounced his life's
work on 23rd June, 1633, a good twenty-three years after he had
seen with his own eyes proof of the correctness of Copernicus's
assertions.

He had saved his life as he shuffled over the large blue
flagstones back into the sunshine. He would not be burned at
the stake like his fellow-scientist Giordano Bruno. He would
spend the few years that remained to him in quietness, restricted
in his freedom of movement. Outside the monastery he deeply
inhaled the warm summer air. He shook his head fiercely and
mumbled to himself 'It does move. . . .' At least that is what has
been passed down to us.

And it does move. Galileo Galilei was right, as Copernicus
had been as well. The earth is not the fixed and immutable
centre of the universe around which the moon, the sun, the
planets and stars are supposed to rotate, as the old Greek

Ptolemy had taught centuries before. His view had been generally accepted for centuries and not merely because the Church had accepted it, since it agreed with what was taught in the Bible.

Nicolaus Copernicus refuted completely the time-honoured view of Ptolemy, which had been ennobled through the centuries and refined by generations of scholars. In the spring of 1543, a few weeks before his death, he published his book *De revolutionibus orbium coelestium* (*Concerning the rotation of heavenly bodies*), in which he stated that the sun and not the earth is the centre of the solar system and that the earth moves with the other planets around the sun. Copernicus reduced the earth from the great centre of the universe to an insignificant sphere somewhere in the space around the sun.

Copernicus was aware that his assertions would cause enormous disturbances and that they would meet with violent opposition, particularly amongst the clergy. He did not therefore publicize his views in the years after 1506 when he arrived at his new picture of the world. He waited for thirty-seven years, until shortly before his death. The storms he had foreseen did in fact come—but they could no longer harm Nicolaus Copernicus.

In spite of all opposition, the new theory gained ground. Galileo was the man who proved that Copernicus had been right. This took place after he had heard of the invention of the telescope. He made a telescope from a cardboard cylinder and a few small lenses. It was a very imperfect instrument that he pointed towards the sky, yet he saw mountains on the moon and spots on the sun. He saw that the planet Venus showed just the same type of phases as the moon which was possible only if Venus revolved round the sun and not round the earth. And he saw, on 7th January, 1610, that four moons revolved round the planet Jupiter, resulting in a solar system in miniature!

Galileo was enthusiastic. The correctness of Copernicus's theory had been proved. He knew, however, about the opposition in the ranks of the clergy. He therefore called in the Church authorities, in order to let them see with their own eyes that they were wrong. The opposition was, nevertheless, too great. The priests even refused to touch Galileo's diabolical instrument. Their refusal was the beginning of a martyrdom which was to lead Galileo to the hall of the Santa Maria sopra Minerva monastery in Rome.

More than three centuries have passed since then. Galileo was followed by Newton and hundreds of other scholars. They continued to add to the correct picture of the solar system. There is no longer any disagreement about it, even the Church has dropped its objections.

During the last few decades astronomers had not paid all that much attention to the solar system. They had preferred to turn their eyes to things a long way beyond it. Only after World War II has the system of the sun, planets and moons again become the focus of interest, since very rapid technical developments have begun to offer the possibility of visiting other parts of this system. The path once begun by Galileo has now led to Wernher von Braun and his colleagues, both American and Russian, many of the latter working in anonymity. Rockets have travelled farther and farther from the earth and appeared to be in a position to launch artificial satellites in orbits around the earth and the first artificial planets have been born. The next step was to reach the moon, followed by circling it. It is now fairly certain, according to most experts, that man will also be able to tear himself away from the earth. How far he will be able to go will be discussed later.

Man is going to leave the earth at a time when his own planet is not yet completely known to him. It may perhaps sound strange, but scholars know relatively more about the moon than about the earth. They know fairly well what the inside of the sun looks like, but are still for the most part groping in the dark concerning conditions at the centre of the earth. It is strange that perhaps just by leaving the earth scientists will be in a position to find out more about our home. It has appeared that we shall be able to derive more facts about the earth from the information obtained by artificial satellites than had at first sight seemed likely.

It is of course incorrect to say that we are completely ignorant. Science is nevertheless anxious to find out the precise details, and these have not yet all been discovered.

That is, after all, not absolutely necessary for an overall picture, but it should generally be realized that the earth is not what it appears to us to be. This is accepted in the civilized world, although there are still quite a number of people who have difficulty in realizing that the world is not a flat object, but a sphere. We live on an enormous football which is slightly flattened on two sides, a football with a diameter of almost 13,000 kilometres and a mass of 6 quadrillion kilogrammes. A footballer would certainly have to have very strong legs to be able to score a goal with this ball.

Since the diameter is so large, the curvature of the earth's surface is to our eyes so slight as to be imperceptible. Consequently we have the impression that we are walking on a flat surface. Photos, taken from rockets at a very great height, nevertheless show clearly that our impression is incorrect. The earth is, therefore, an enormous sphere which revolves around its axis. That axis does not really exist, it is merely an imaginary line which runs from the North Pole to the South Pole through the heart of the sphere.

The earth revolves around this axis in about 24 hours.[1] Being continually shone upon by the sun, all parts of it are exposed to sunlight in turn—and this explains the phenomenon of day and night. The earth describes an orbit around the sun in about 365 days and in doing this assumes a variable position with regard to the sun as it speeds on its way at a velocity of almost 30 kilometres per second—this accounting for the seasons.

One would not think so, but no less than 97% of our earth is liquid and boiling hot. The materials at the very centre of the earth—probably for the most part metals—are liquid since they are at temperatures of many hundreds of degrees centigrade. Many scholars consider that all the material on the earth was once as hot as this. It was probably in fact gaseous. The gas became liquid when it condensed and the liquid sphere has acquired a thin crust during the course of millions of years of slow cooling.

This crust is consequently only an extremely small part of all terrestrial matter, 3% in fact. The crust is the place where we live and work, struggle and dream, love and suffer. Life on the earth has only an extremely small region at its disposal. We should be scorched a few hundred kilometres below the earth's surface. Yet a few kilometres above its surface we should freeze—and suffocate, for the layer of air which

[1] Further details about the earth and moon are given in the Appendix.

24

surrounds the earth is extremely cold and rarefied at that height. Life is confined between two limits which are a few kilometres apart.

We should really have said 'was confined,' for since man can launch artificial satellites and rockets to the moon he is theoretically also in a position to transfer life to regions outside his own, at least for a short time. A long way outside it? Has man conquered space and is he now in a position to undertake large-scale journeys into space?

Before giving an answer to this and similar questions, it will be advisable to review matters in perspective. By doing this, we arrive at surprising conclusions.

A very useful method of getting the relationships in perspective is that of reduction. How do these relationships appear if we imagine the earth, for example, as a sphere the size of a man, that is with a diameter of about 1·70 metres? Mont Blanc, the enormous mountain on the Swiss–French border, will have a height of about half a millimetre on such a sphere. The highest mountain on the earth will be a spot somewhat higher than one millimetre, this being the majestic Mount Everest which is 9,000 metres high. The greatest depth which has ever been measured in the sea, namely 10 kilometres near the Philippines, would be a scratch about one millimetre deep on our reduced model of the earth. Aeroplanes would reach an average height of half a millimetre, and an artificial satellite, reaching a maximum distance of 25,000 kilometres from the earth's surface, would be a speck of dust about 2 metres from the earth in our model. What about rockets to the moon? The moon would be about 50 metres away, which is quite a distance. The sun is, however, a few tens of *kilometres* farther, not to speak of the stars.

Bearing these relationships in mind, we can give an answer to the question. No, technicians have not conquered space with their artificial satellites and rockets to the moon. They will not even have done this once they have landed on the moon, for when they are there, they will be in the position of a man who is about to make a journey round the world and has succeeded, with great effort, in rising from his chair and is standing in front of his sitting-room window looking out to see whether he will have to take his raincoat.

25

Man will still be at home when he is on the moon. The moon shares the pleasures and sorrows of the earth. Completing its orbit around our sphere in one month, the moon follows our planet on its path round the sun. It cannot escape from the earth's force of attraction and live its own life.

The moon and artificial satellites move around the earth which, in its turn, moves round the sun. How is it that artificial satellites do not fall straight back on to the earth, that the moon does not fall upon the earth, that the earth is not pulled towards the sun to perish in the intense heat which prevails there?

It was the patriarch of classical science, the Englishman, Isaac Newton, who found the explanation. Tradition has it that he was lying on his back in his garden one warm evening and saw the moon shining through the branches of an apple-tree. Suddenly one of the apples fell to the ground with a thud, and Newton thought, at least according to tradition, which always seems to know what people think, 'Why does that apple fall while the moon does not?'

Newton began to consider the matter and came to the conclusion that the moon falls just as the apple does, but the apple falls on to the earth and *the moon falls around the earth*. This is also true of the artificial satellites, as well as of the earth as far as the sun is concerned.

The position with the moon is the same as that with a stone which is thrown. The stone describes an arc before it reaches the ground. The moon also describes a similar arc during its fall, but that arc runs 'parallel' to the curved surface of the earth. This is why the moon falls 'parallel' to the surface of the earth and does not therefore fall down. The reason why artificial satellites fall sooner or later is because they do not move in a complete vacuum as does the moon. They meet a certain amount of resistance from the highest parts of the atmosphere, which reduces their speed so that their path gradually comes to resemble that of a stone which has been thrown. If we are ultimately successful in launching an artificial satellite into a real vacuum, then it will continue to circle round the earth for ever, just as the moon does.

For ever? That is not quite correct. In the first place the earth will not exist 'for ever.' Also, the moon's orbit is not constant. Every year the average distance between the earth and the moon becomes a few centimetres greater. This does not make any difference during one human life. Yet, in astronomy, where people work with millions of years as the grocer does with pennies, we cannot neglect these centimetres. As far as can be made out, the moon has always been increasing its distance from the earth. In the past the distance between these two heavenly bodies must therefore have been much smaller. There must even have been a time, according to some scholars, when that distance was zero, in other words, when the earth and the moon were one. At a rough estimate that must have been a good 2 milliard years ago.

According to this theory, the moon separated from the earth at the time when our planet was still completely liquid, or when only a mere beginning had been made with the formation of a crust. Some scholars accept this latter explanation. They even consider they can point to the place where the moon's cradle stood. The Pacific Ocean is said to be the scar which mother earth has to show as a result of the birth of her child. If the earth was, however, still completely liquid during this birth, we could now no longer find any trace of it.

In recent years quite a different and far more plausible theory has been gaining ground. Its adherents deny that the moon is the earth's child. Their calculations show, in fact, that an amount of matter torn away from the earth would never have been able to form a moon. The earth would, at the most, have been able to acquire a ring, more or less like the planet Saturn. The new theories say that the earth and the moon arose close to, yet independently of one another as a double planet. They also consider that these two bodies were not formed in the red-hot state, but in the cold state by the clotting together of material which remained when the sun was formed.

Whether it is a child of the earth or not, the moon now revolves in its orbit around the earth at an average distance of 385,000 kilometres, giving evidence of its presence by causing the tides in our oceans. The moon rotates round its axis as does the earth. It does this differently however. It rotates around its axis in precisely the same time in which it completes its orbit around the earth. This means that it always turns the same face towards the earth. Somewhat more than half the surface of the moon is known to man—the side which is turned away from the earth has never yet been seen by a human eye. Photos taken by the Russian 'Lunik III' of the far side of the moon suggest that it is even more monotonous than the side we know.

The moon is much smaller than the earth. Its volume is about a fiftieth of that of our planet. Since its mass is much less than 'ours,' the moon does not have sufficient force of attraction to hold an atmosphere. It probably had one 'in the beginning,' but the gases have escaped into space. This is a pity for the athletes amongst us, who would otherwise be able to set up some fine records on the moon. The moon's force of attraction is a sixth of that on the earth. What weighs a kilogramme here would weigh about 150 grammes there. An athlete would be able to jump 4 or 5 metres without any difficulty.

But no, the moon is an inhospitable, terrible place for man. There is no atmosphere and consequently no sound either. There is no water. The surface consists of dry volcanic ash covering a substratum of stones. There are mountains and very large craters which can be clearly distinguished from the earth using a good telescope. The craters were probably formed at an earlier stage during volcanic eruptions.

It is hot and cold on the moon, hot during the fourteen terrestrial days when the sun is continuously above the horizon and causes the temperature to rise to about 100° C. The ground is then boiling hot. It is cold during the remaining fourteen days when night prevails and the temperature of the ground falls to below −100° C. The position on the moon is, therefore, the same as on the earth, one half of the time is day, the other night, and *vice versa*. The differences are, however, very very great. . . .

Since there is no air, there is no 'weather' on the moon. In the sun, which can never shelter behind clouds, it is boiling hot; just outside it, in the shadow of a rock for example, it is icy cold. Nothing ever changes on the moon, except perhaps that here and there a piece of rock falls loose and rolls down. This is caused by the effect of alternating contraction and expansion in the rock during the change from day and night, or by the falling of meteors, or by rockets sent from the earth to the moon. . . .

No air, no water, no sound. Extreme heat and extreme cold. Ash and stone. This all means that there is no life, no plants, no animals, nothing. The moon is a completely lifeless place and probably has always been like that.

Astronomers have been able to make such accurate observations of the moon with their powerful telescopes that they were able to draw maps of the visible part of its surface which rival in precision atlases of the earth.

This knowledge will soon be of use when the first travellers to the moon land there. Do not ask what sense there is in expending enormous amounts of money and energy in getting to a heavenly body which has nothing to offer man except ash and stone and terror. The question means nothing as such. Science does not ask about its own use, it merely wants to know.

In any case an expedition to the moon will provide useful indications for possible future ventures, compared with which the journey to the moon will pale into insignificance. I refer to the exploration of the neighbouring planets.

CHAPTER III

The large sword flashed down twice, and two heads rolled into the sand. The astronomers Hi and Ho had paid with their lives for neglecting their duty, and the sun had as a result almost fallen a victim to an awful dragon. They had eaten and drunk, celebrated and slept, had let the calendar become muddled and failed to warn their emperor that a dragon would once again ensnare the sun.

Chung Kang, emperor of China, had only one punishment for this atrocious negligence, namely death. There had been a dreadful panic. Throughout the immense Chinese empire the peasants and citizens, nobles and soldiers had seen with horror that the sun was disappearing in the middle of the day. The shining disc became smaller and smaller, a dragon was engaged in devouring the source of all life. The sun had of course often been threatened in the past, but then the astrologers had given the warning in time, so that all China could help the sun. The dragon was frightened by drums and hooters, shouting and dancing, so that he quickly spat the sun out again. This time, however, nobody had been prepared. People picked up what they could in order to make a noise and drive the dragon away. Fortunately they succeeded, just in time. The dragon spat out the sun, but Hi and Ho had to pay for their neglect with their lives.

This all happened about four thousand years ago on 22nd October, 2137 B.C., towards midday to be precise.

The movements of the heavenly bodies are known so accurately that astronomers have been able to calculate the date of the solar eclipse which cost Hi and Ho their lives and which is recorded in one of the oldest Chinese writings extant. The solar system—as will also appear later—is an extremely accurate timepiece, and almost everything taking place in it can be calculated by astronomers well in advance—and, if necessary, a long time after it has happened.

This latter possibility is, for example, very important for historians. Reports of solar eclipses are found again and again amongst the data they have concerning kings, battles, victories and changes in the state of government of ancient races. These eclipses were so startling and made such a deep impression on observers that most historians of the past at least recorded a short note about them. This meant that modern historians could, with the help of astronomers, obtain all sorts of information that would otherwise have remained unknown to them. They knew, for example, that there had been a battle between the Medes and the Lydians at the beginning of the sixth century B.C. The exact date was not known. It was, however, stated in an old document that an eclipse of the sun began during the battle and caused terror and alarm amongst the participants. On the basis of this information astronomers fixed the date of the battle, namely 28th May, 585 B.C. Another example is the defeat of the Athenians in their battle against Syracuse. This time it was not a solar eclipse, but an eclipse of the moon, which also played a decisive part in the result of the battle! The Athenians were on the point of raising the siege of Syracuse and sailing away when the eclipse began. They became afraid and waited. This gave the people of Syracuse the opportunity of destroying the whole of the Athenian fleet. The date of the eclipse and of the battle was 27th August, 413 B.C

An eclipse of the sun is also mentioned in the Bible. The ninth verse of the eighth chapter of the Book of Amos in the Old Testament reads : 'And it shall come to pass in that day, saith the Lord God, that I will cause the sun to go down at noon, and I will darken the earth in the clear day.' This probably refers to the eclipse on 15th June, 763 B.C.

For the past seventy years or so astronomers have had a complete handbook of eclipses. The Austrian doctor and astronomer, Theodor von Oppolzer, together with a number of his pupils, calculated all the solar and lunar eclipses between 1207 B.C. and A.D. 2161, resulting in a total of 13,000—8,000 of the sun and 5,000 of the moon. They are listed in his book

31

Kanon der Finsternisse, which appeared in 1887, not only with the date and time, but also with the place and duration. It will be realized what an enormous number of calculations this involved when it is known that the 'sums' filled 243 thick, folio-sized volumes.

It may be assumed that von Oppolzer knew very much more about the phenomenon of an eclipse than did his poor colleagues Hi and Ho. One very important conclusion can however be drawn from the old Chinese story. Hi and Ho had not announced the eclipse, but they could have done so if they had performed their high duty conscientiously. In other words, astronomers in the Chinese empire a good four thousand years ago were well acquainted with the movements of the heavenly bodies. This certainly says something for the level of civilization in the Far East at a time when there was no question of any scientific knowledge at all in Europe.

Well, the Chinese at that time believed that a dragon ensnared the sun. They had no idea that a more or less fortuitous view was playing a trick on them. Modern man knows better, yet little has really changed since the death of Hi and Ho. Even today there are millions of people who see with terror and trembling that some monster or another comes too close to the sun and think that the monster can be chased away by shouting, whistling and dancing. Let us be quite honest about it. How many people in our own country would not, to say the least, feel uncomfortable and a little afraid if they were to see a total eclipse of the sun? And that is quite understandable, for a total eclipse is one of the most powerful spectacles which nature offers man, a scene in which she reveals all her magnificence.[1]

Slowly the dark disc of the moon moves in front of the body of the sun. It happens so gradually that we scarcely notice it. The noisy life on the earth continues as usual. Only when more than half the sun is covered do we sense something strange. The light becomes different, and the shadows become sharper. The flowers close their calyces, the birds seek out their nests. It becomes a little cooler. Suddenly there is a breeze. There is still just a very small crescent of the sun in the darkened sky in which the stars are now shining. The cattle become restive,

[1] There is a list in the Appendix of all the total eclipses of the sun between 1962 and 2000, taken from von Oppolzer's *Kanon der Finsternisse*.

dogs begin to whine. Suddenly the eclipse is total. It is night, in the middle of the day. The transition from semi-totality to totality is enormous. There is no longer any trace of daylight. The dark disc of the moon stands in the sky, amidst the stars and planets. It is surrounded by the magnificent radiance of the corona or the sun's atmosphere, which is normally invisible because the body of the sun shines completely over it. In most cases after a very short time the first ray of light shoots towards the earth again. Day rapidly returns. The flowers open their calyces. Normal life resumes its course.

Solar and lunar eclipses are really nothing special. The sun, earth and moon describe their orbits with unswerving regularity and about sixty-six times every century the moon stands exactly between the sun and the earth, and almost as often the earth finds itself precisely between the sun and the moon. There is consequently an average of sixty-six years with and thirty-four years without an eclipse every century.

Solar eclipses however always occur at different places on the earth and a total eclipse can normally not be seen at one and the same place more than once every three hundred years.

The position is quite different with total eclipses of the moon. Every place on the earth will see one every three years on an average. A total lunar eclipse is unfortunately not a very spectacular scene. A special watch must be kept for it, otherwise it will not be noticed.

This difference is strange, but not that strange if we bear in mind the essential difference between solar and lunar eclipses. An eclipse of the sun is a perspective phenomenon, and an eclipse of the moon is a real one. Let us see exactly what the difference is.

The earth describes an orbit around the sun, as the moon does around the earth. We can imagine that the earth's orbit lies in a flat plane, in the centre of which is the sun. That plane is called the ecliptic. If the orbital plane of the moon were to coincide precisely with the ecliptic, that is to say if the moon, earth and sun were always to be in the same flat plane, then the moon would be precisely between the sun and the earth every time it is 'new.' We would then have a solar eclipse every month. This is not so, since the orbital planes of the earth and the moon do not coincide, but are at an acute angle to one another. This means that during a 'new moon' the moon passes in most cases 'above' or 'below' the sun, as seen from the earth. Yet if the moon stands where the orbital planes of the earth and moon intersect, then the moon, earth and sun lie in a straight line. The mere fact that the discs of the moon and the sun are about the same size when seen from the earth then causes a total eclipse. Of course the disc of the sun is very much larger than that of the moon—four hundred times in fact—but it is also very much farther away—also four hundred times. This coincidence means that the discs both appear to us to be about the same size, so that the dark disc of the moon precisely covers that of the sun as far as our eyes are concerned, at least if we are at the place where the moon casts its shadow on the earth. Nothing happens outside that shadow, the sun merely continues to shine as usual.

A total eclipse of the moon nevertheless means that the moon ceases to radiate light. The moon has, after all, no light of its own. It is a dark sphere which merely reflects the light of the sun. Moonlight is second-hand light. If however the earth is between the moon and the sun, the light of the sun cannot reach the moon, since the moon then comes within the shadow of the earth. Then the moon no longer shines! In other words, wherever one may be on the earth, one will be able to see the eclipse, provided that the moon is above the horizon. In most cases this is the position on almost half the earth's surface. At one place the moon will be high in the sky, at another it will have just risen, elsewhere it will be about to set—but wherever it is visible the eclipse will be seen. This explains the difference in frequency of occurrence of solar and lunar eclipses.

Let us now consider an eclipse of the sun.

The moon casts its shadow on the earth. Every object that is illuminated from one side casts two shadows behind itself, the sharply tapering full shadow or umbra, which is very deep, and the somewhat wider half-shadow or penumbra, which is less deep and becomes lighter and lighter towards its edge. The moon has no reason to behave differently, and it casts its umbra and penumbra on the earth. At the place where the umbra, which is shaped like a cone, touches the earth, we no longer see anything of the sun. Sitting right near the cone, in other words in the penumbra, a small part of the sun can be seen. There it is

34

not, consequently, as dark as in the umbra, and the farther we move towards the edge of the penumbra, the lighter it becomes, or rather the less the sun is eclipsed and the more sunlight we 'retain.'

As a result of the path of the moon and of the rotation of the axis of the earth, the umbra eclipses the sun not only at one place on the earth's surface, but glides over the earth, just as we sometimes see the shadow of a low-flying aircraft gliding over the ground. The regions which successively come within the umbra are called collectively the region of totality. Let us take a recent example, namely the eclipse of 2nd October, 1959. This began in the morning at Philadelphia on the east coast of America and moved south-eastwards over the Atlantic Ocean via the Canary Islands to the west coast of Africa, hastened diagonally across Africa and ended in the late afternoon to the east of the east coast of Africa in the Indian Ocean. The eclipse consequently moved at a high speed approximately from west to east, covering many thousands of kilometres in a few hours. Each place in the heart of this region of totality experienced a total eclipse during the seventy-four seconds which the umbra required to pass over it. Perhaps we may one day advance to the extent that we shall be able to keep up with the eclipse in an aeroplane, taking off where it begins and landing where it finishes, and between these points flying over the zone of totality at the same speed as the umbra. Astronomers will then no longer have to be satisfied with a few seconds or minutes, but will be able to observe the eclipse for hours on end from an aeroplane!

A total eclipse does not always last only seventy-four seconds, varying from a few seconds to several minutes in duration. Under the most favourable conditions—which are extremely rare—an eclipse can even last for more than seven minutes at one and the same place. This depends on the distances from the sun and moon. The orbits of the earth and moon are not circles, but ellipses, and at certain points the earth is closer to the sun than at others. The same also applies to the moon and the earth. An eclipse of the sun has its maximum duration when the earth is as far as possible from the sun and the moon is as near as possible to the earth. In that case the umbra of the moon is as long as possible, and not only the narrow extreme point of that umbra, but also a piece of the wider part falls on the earth. The maximum width is about 300 kilometres. Under these circumstances the ratio of magnitude between the sun and the moon is also as favourable as possible as far as the moon is concerned. The sun, being farther away than normal, appears smaller, and the moon, being closer than usual, appears larger. The passage of the moon in front of the sun then has its maximum duration.

But what if the position is the other way about, namely if the earth is as close as possible to the sun and the moon is at the same time as far as possible from the earth? Then the umbra just misses touching the earth's surface, and we see something that happens only in seven out of every hundred eclipses. The disc of the sun is then somewhat larger than that of the moon, the outer edge of the sun remains visible around the moon, and there is a shining ring in the sky. The eclipse is not total, but annular.

Other variations are also possible. The top of the umbra can reach just beyond the earth, farther north than the North Pole or farther south than the South Pole, strange as it may sound. Then the eclipse is not total anywhere on the earth.

But enough of these variations. They are really of interest only to the expert. It is sufficient for the layman to know what he sees and what causes it, namely that powerful and miraculous natural phenomenon which continues to attract man's attention to the majesty of creation, a majesty which formerly frightened the Chinese as it now does many races, but which also always makes an impression even on seasoned astronomers. Here is the admission of the Austrian astronomer, Professor Dr. O. Thomas:

'I too once experienced a total eclipse of the sun, in 1932 during an international meeting of astronomers in North America, near the Canadian border. The great fairy-tale affected me so much that my whole body was trembling when the daylight returned. I admitted this experience to one of the solar scientists. He answered: "Don't worry, my friend, I was trembling all through it".'

CHAPTER IV

THE PLANETARY SYSTEM, AN ACCURATE TIMEPIECE. LEVERRIER DISCOVERS NEPTUNE WITH PENCIL AND PAPER. A JOURNEY THROUGH BARREN WORLDS

Johann Gottfried Galle focused the telescope of the Berlin observatory. He once again compared the position with the information on the paper he held in his hand and which he had received that same day, 23rd September, 1846, from his French colleague, the astronomer Urbain Leverrier. Galle then looked through the telescope at the spot in the sky which had been indicated to him by his French colleague. Almost beside it he saw a small, faintly shining disc. Galle once again made an adjustment on his instrument, but the disc remained a disc. What he was seeing was not a star, but a planet, a child of the sun. Galle saw the eighth planet of our solar system, which was later to be given the name Neptune, a planet which had up till then been unknown to the inhabitants of the earth.

In order to make this discovery, Galle had merely to look at a spot in the sky of which he had been informed in writing by Leverrier, who in fact *knew* that there must be a planet at that spot—he had worked it out with pencil and paper. For months he had been sitting making calculations, filling hundreds of sheets of paper. When he was at last able to finish his calculations on 31st August, 1846, Urbain Leverrier had discovered a new planet, millions of kilometres away from his study, with nothing more than a pencil and paper.

He was so certain of the correctness of his calculation that he did not even trouble to sit at a telescope to convince himself that he was right. It was enough for him to send a letter to his colleague Galle in Berlin on 18th September, 1846. It did not occur to him that he would look a fool if Galle did not find anything.

Admiration for Leverrier as discoverer of Neptune was of course general. It was also completely deserved. But yet. . . .

Life can sometimes be cruel, and thus it was to the young English student of astronomy, John Couch Adams. He was twenty-six when in 1845 he handed a bundle of papers to the director of the observatory at Greenwich with the announcement that he had calculated on those papers the position of an as yet unknown planet. The director was, however, not interested. He put the papers somewhere in a cupboard and forgot about them. If he had only taken the trouble to look at them or at least to mention something about them to others, Adams, and not Leverrier, would have been the discoverer of Neptune. It turned out later that Adams's calculation had been correct and was also more concise, for he had needed only about half as many calculations as Leverrier to reach the same conclusion, and he was also about a year sooner with his calculation!

After this, certain mathematicians tried in the same way to find the ninth planet the existence of which was assumed. They were not successful however. The ninth planet, Pluto, was observed more or less by chance by the American amateur astronomer Clyde Tombaugh in 1930. And the tenth? It is not impossible that there is a tenth. Perhaps there are even more. In any case astronomers have not yet been able to find a tenth planet, and it is therefore generally considered that our sun has nine planets, namely, *Mercury, Venus, Earth, Mars, Jupiter, Saturn, Uranus, Neptune* and *Pluto*. All these planets keep so accurately to the laws of nature that Leverrier and Adams were successful merely by applying these laws on paper. The planetary system is a very accurate timepiece.

It is now about time to discover what a planet is. The naked eye can see hundreds of sparkling points of light in the sky at night. Which are stars and which are planets?

Stars are suns like our sun, that is enormous glowing balls of gas which merely appear different from our sun because they are billions of kilometres away, while the sun, astronomically speaking, is quite close to us. If the sun were as far away as they are, it would appear as a star to us and would be indistinguishable from one in every way.

Planets are not suns. They are firm bodies like the earth

which describe orbits around the sun as the earth does. They are not billions of kilometres away, but always remain in the direct neighbourhood of the sun and consequently of the earth. Their distances apart do not amount to more than several million kilometres, while a billion is a million million. The stars are therefore millions of times farther away than the planets.

Planets are satellites of the sun. They do not give any light themselves, as the stars do, but have to put up with the light which the sun allows to fall on them and which they partly reflect. A planet therefore gives millions of times less light than a star, but since it is millions of times closer, the naked eye sees hardly any difference in intensity between the light of the stars and that of the planets. A substantial difference is, however, seen with a telescope, even with a not very powerful one. In a telescope a planet is seen as a small shining disc, while a star remains a point, even in the most powerful telescope. A star is so far away that we cannot see it as a sphere.

The solar system is, consequently, an enormous, glowing sphere of gas, a star, with nine small, solid spheres at various distances from it which move in various times in orbits around the star, at the same time rotating on their own axes. They are forced to follow their orbits since the sun attracts them, in the same way as a stone at the end of a cord describes a path around the man who is swinging it around him.

As far as we know, the sun has nine planets. It is possible that there used to be ten, but we will discuss that point later.

Nine planets which all came into existence around the same sun must certainly have much in common and must resemble one another very much, at least one would imagine so on the surface. This is not so. Although no human being has so far ever visited one of the other planets, astronomers know enough to be able to say that there are enormous differences between the sun's children. Almost the only similarity is that they are all built up from precisely the same substances. This is not surprising, for it is certain that in the section of the universe which we can see there are no elements other than those which we know on the earth. It is only the proportion in which the elements occur on the planets which is different.

Let us have a look at the planets by building a space-ship which can attain a speed of 10,000 kilometres per hour and which is therefore ten times faster than an average jet fighter. We will leave from the sun and travel from one planet to the other. We will assume that the planets, as seen from the sun, are all in a row one after the other, which is of course incorrect, since they describe their orbits at various speeds and at various distances from the sun.

We will leave the sun at a speed of 10,000 kilometres per hour. After 5,800 hours, that is after 241 days, we arrive at Mercury, a sphere 58 million kilometres from the sun with a diameter of 5,000 kilometres. Mercury is therefore much smaller than the earth which has a diameter of 12,757 kilometres. How like the moon Mercury is! It is a mass of stone without water and without air. There is a thick layer of ash and dust on its surface. There are craters and mountains. Nothing points to life which, in the earthly sense of the word, is completely impossible on Mercury, all the more so since this planet has, like the moon, a so-called bound rotation, always turning the same face to the sun, as the moon does to the earth. This means that one half of Mercury always has day and the other half night. And what a day and what a night! On the side facing the sun there is an average temperature of 330° centigrade, a temperature at which various metals already melt. On the side of eternal night, on the other hand, it is a good 150° below zero. Only in a narrow region on the border between day and night do temperatures occur which can be compared with those of the earth.

No, Mercury has never known life and will never know it. The planet is completely inhospitable to man. Let us therefore get into our space-ship again.

It took us 241 days to reach Mercury from the sun. We must add a further 209 days to reach our next port of call, Venus, the mysterious planet situated at an average of 108 million kilometres from the sun and functioning as an evening and morning star for the inhabitants of the earth. This planet has many points of similarity with the earth; its volume is almost the same, its average density is just a little less and its force of gravity is therefore almost the same. This is however the end of the points of similarity, at least as far as we know. For we still know very little about Venus. The planet is enveloped in a very thick, uninterrupted cloud-cover. This of course proves the presence of an atmosphere, but at the same time prevents us obtaining a view of the planet's surface. Since drifting masses of cloud do not provide any point of reference, we do not know the time taken by Venus to rotate round its axis. There are certainly indications that Venus would have an axis rotation period almost equal to that of the earth, but those indications are vague and lack proof.

It is at least known that the atmosphere of Venus is definitely unsuited for human beings. There is perhaps a trace of oxygen, the gas which makes all animal and human life on the earth possible, but there is in any case a large amount of carbon dioxide which is harmful to man in high concentrations. The presence of life in the terrestrial sense must therefore be considered improbable. There is, however, something we do not know, namely anything about the surface of Venus. A calculation of the surface temperature gave a value of $57°$ C., but this was based on so many estimates, approximations and faulty observations that the result must be viewed with many reservations. Under its cloud-cover this planet therefore seems to be a sort of enormous hot-house where man could not exist for long, even if the rest of the conditions were to allow his presence.

Our space-ship must therefore carry us on quickly. The journey has lasted 450 days so far. We now add 173 days and arrive, 623 days after our departure from the sun, at the following planet where we can take a deep breath, for we are home, it is our planet Earth. It has nothing to offer for our present purpose, so we continue, for a further 327 days, at 10,000 kilometres per hour.

And 950 days after leaving the sun we arrive at the planet which has fascinated man most during the last half-century, namely Mars. At least on Mars there are canals which must have been dug by intelligent beings. Mars is a planet with a civilization, much more highly developed than that of the earth, and we cannot form any idea of the technical achievements of the inhabitants of Mars. This was all firmly asserted by the uninitiated a few decades ago—and some of those who were initiated also seem to have believed it. At any rate the Italian astronomer, Schiaparelli, had in his telescope seen a pattern of straight lines on the surface of Mars. These must be canals

41

which conducted the little water on the planet from one place to another. These canals must have been constructed and therefore . . .

Science soon dealt with the canals and inhabitants of Mars. The canals appeared to be an optical illusion—the better telescopes became, the less there remained of the lines. Similarly there was no further mention of the inhabitants of Mars.

Nevertheless our neighbour, which sends us a weak reddish light, which has won for it the name of the god of war, does seem to harbour life. The most recent investigations indicate that Mars has a vegetation of lichens, being extremely primitive plants which have had to struggle hard for their existence. The earth is consequently not the only planet with organic life—it is not unique in the universe.

Astronomers have devoted a great deal of attention to Mars and more is known about this planet than about any other. There are even detailed maps of its surface, like those which have been made of the moon. Mars has an atmosphere, but it does not seem to contain any free oxygen. Even if there is oxygen, its amount is too small to be detected with the present instruments we have on the earth. There is certainly combined oxygen, for there is water, a very small amount, however, which does not occur as liquid, but as frost. The polar caps of Mars are white during the season which is winter for each of them. This is not due, as on the earth, to enormous amounts of snow and ice, but to the frost which has lodged in a thin layer on the surface.

Mars has seasons. There is water. There is an atmosphere. Could man live there? Perhaps, but certainly not without various aids, for even if there were oxygen in the atmosphere, the atmosphere of Mars is rarer than the air on the highest mountains on the earth and even on those mountains we need an oxygen mask. The average temperature is $-15°$ C., in other words tolerable for man. The force of gravity is a third of that on the earth—Mars is the smallest planet but one—and it is therefore pleasant to go walking there. One could even go for walks in the moonlight, for Mars has two moons, Phobus and Deimos, two small spheres which revolve round the planet relatively quickly.

For the sake of completeness we should mention a Russian

theory, namely that Phobos and Deimos are not natural satellites of Mars. Russian astronomers consider that they are artificial satellites which were brought into orbit around Mars millions of years ago by an intelligent inhabitant of the planet who has since become extinct, just as artificial satellites now circulate around the earth, having been launched there by man. Western astronomers have nevertheless violently rejected this theory and shortly after its publication Americans spoke of it as an 'April-fool-day's joke.' The Russians have, however, stated that they are serious. Perhaps a future space-flight to Mars will provide the final answer. If Mars were formerly inhabited, it must still show traces of it. Who knows what surprises this planet still has in store for inquisitive man. Pleasant . . . or otherwise.

It is difficult to leave Mars, even if we do not need to take leave of intelligent beings. We must continue in order to learn about the rest of the family of planets. We now seem to be plunging into nothingness in our space-ship. We travel and travel, 10,000 kilometres every hour, and only after 2,292 days does the following planet loom up before us. This is Jupiter, the big brother amongst the sun's children, larger than all the other planets put together, being on an average 778 million kilometres from the sun. Jupiter is a giant sphere with a diameter of 140,000 kilometres and a volume which is 1,310 times as large as that of the earth. Jupiter contains 318 times as much matter as our terrestrial sphere, and it should not be thought that one would not notice a landing on Jupiter. The force of gravity on Jupiter is in fact a good two-and-a-half times as strong as that here on earth. A man who weighs 80 kilogrammes here would weigh more than 200 on Jupiter. He would collapse under his own weight. This would not matter much to man, for Jupiter is an inhospitable place in other respects as well, and will always be inaccessible to man. The planet has an enormous atmosphere, but it contains very unpleasant gases as far as man is concerned, such as ammonia and methane, better known as marsh gas. The 'air' on Jupiter also appears to contain a large amount of hydrogen. And, as if this were not enough, the most recent discovery is that Jupiter is surrounded by a zone of very strong and probably lethal radioactivity.

It is always dim there, for the sun is so far away that its light, which has to pass through a thick circle of vapour, scarcely shines on the surface. It is also very cold, 130° below zero on an average. The surface of Jupiter consists of a layer of ice which is thousands of *kilometres* thick. It is not known what lies underneath it. There are all sorts of suppositions concerning the nature of the core of Jupiter, but we really know nothing at all about it. In any case, it is very terrible there, and the no fewer than twelve moons which accompany this giant cannot do anything about it.

It is now 3,242 days since we started our journey and we have visited five of the nine planets. Are we now more than half-way to the border of our solar system? By no means. We are now about an eighth of the way to Pluto, for the farther we come the farther the planets are apart.

Let us now travel to the next planet which is Saturn. This takes a further 2,675 days from Jupiter. It is scarcely worth the trouble, for Saturn, although not as large as Jupiter, is ninety-five times as 'heavy' as the earth and shows almost the same picture as its larger brother. Poisonous gases, ice, darkness. We do not even need to think about life here, let alone talk about it. This applies in fact to all the other planets we still have to visit.

Nevertheless Saturn has something special about it, namely its rings, which are clearly visible from the earth under favourable circumstances. These consist of dust, stones, pieces of ice, in short of all sorts of large and small pieces of matter which move round the planet in concentric paths. They are probably the remains of a moon which once came too close to the planet and which was broken up by the great force of gravity. Anyway, Saturn should not need to lament the loss of this moon, since it still has nine left.

This is many more than its neighbour Uranus which has to make do with five moons. We reach Uranus 6,041 days after leaving Saturn. It is about six times as small as the ringed planet, but in other respects 'has been served with the same sauce.' Darkness, for the light of the sun only penetrates very faintly here. Cold, for the average temperature is here below −185°. We are now about 2·8 milliard kilometres from the sun.

But we are not finished yet. We have to travel a further 6,750 days in order to reach Neptune, the planet to which Leverrier owes his fame, and then a further 5,875 days to reach Pluto. And, finally standing in the barren world of Pluto, about which we know virtually nothing, we imagine that we are at the edge of our solar system, but then we are forgetting heavenly bodies such as comets which also form part of our solar system and which can be at even farther distances from the sun.

We are standing on Pluto and no longer see the sun. At least, not as the sun. We merely see stars and one of those stars is the sun. Perpetual darkness prevails on the last planet which takes 248 years to complete its orbit around the sun.[1]

Planet? At present yes, but formerly Pluto does not seem to have been a planet, but a moon of Neptune. The American astronomer of Dutch origin, G. P. Kuiper, has in any case stated that he has information which indicates that Pluto has promoted itself from the status of moon to that of planet by escaping from Neptune and choosing its own orbit around the sun.

On Pluto, the 'self-made' planet, we are 5·9 milliard kilometres from the sun. At a speed of 10,000 kilometres per hour, at which we could fly round the whole of the earth in four hours, we have travelled from the sun to Pluto in 24,583 days or sixty-seven years, which is almost the normal span of one human life.

It might also perhaps be assumed that we have advanced quite a long way in the conquest of the universe.

In an earlier chapter we said of the moon that a person who has landed there is still only in the position of someone who is on the point of making a journey around the world and has succeeded in rising from his chair and is standing looking out of his sitting-room window to see whether he should take his raincoat or not.

Standing on Pluto we can continue the comparison. The prospective world traveller is now standing at his own front door.

[1] There is a full list of information about all the planets in the Appendix.

CHAPTER V

OUR HOME IN SPACE. A QUEER COLLECTION ... ASTEROIDS, METEORS, COMETS. NATURE PROVED BODE TO BE CORRECT

Johann Eijlert Bode had always said so, and on the first day of the nineteenth century nature itself proved that he had been correct. The German astronomer obtained his planet between Mars and Jupiter on 1st January, 1801. The Italian Piazzi discovered it in the constellation Taurus and called it Ceres.

Was this yet another case of 'predicting a planet,' as with Neptune? No, it was not. Bode, like his colleague Titius, had made a calculation. It had struck him, as well as many other astronomers, that there is between Mars and Jupiter a disproportionately large space in which no planet has chosen its orbit. His calculating led him to postulate a very simple rule about the distances of the planets from the sun. The planets up to and including Uranus were at distances which followed from a mathematical rule, but there was nothing between Mars and Jupiter, while according to Bode's rule there had to be something.

Astronomers have faith in their calculations, and instead of modifying his rule Bode founded a society of which twenty-four astronomers were members and which set out to look for the missing planet.

Piazzi—who was not a member of the club—was the finder. His discovery was certainly modest—the diameter of Ceres is not more than 770 kilometres—but Bode's rule was confirmed, the small planet was located at a distance which followed from Bode's rule. A good year later, in March 1802, a second confirmation followed. The astronomer, Olbers, discovered a further small planet which was given the name Pallas, being situated at about the same average distance from the sun as

46

Ceres. In 1804 Juno joined the company, followed by Vesta in 1807. After that there was no end. More and more small planets were discovered, all more or less in the same orbit as Ceres. They were not really small planets. They seemed rather to be large pieces of rock, varying in diameter from a few metres to a few tens of metres, being at the most a few hundred kilometres. Some did not even appear to be round, but were angular and fanciful in form. They were given the collective name of asteroids or planetoids. Only the largest amongst them were honoured with names of their own, for people did not know where to start with the rest. A few thousand of them are now known.

They describe their orbits around the sun at an average distance of 318 million kilometres. Where did all these large and small blocks of rock come from? The supposition was obvious, asteroids are the remains of a 'real' planet which once passed round the sun between Mars and Jupiter and which burst asunder for one reason or another. This supposition has, up till now, been considered to be the probable truth, although we have no idea what might have led to the destruction of the planet.

The total mass of the asteroids, the total number of which is estimated at about 40,000, is less than that of the moon. If it is in fact a question of the remains of a planet, then that planet must have been very small, unless a large amount of the matter of which it consisted has disappeared into space. Most astronomers consider that this did in fact happen. The Dutch astronomer, Professor Dr. J. H. Oort, even goes so far as to say that not only the asteroids owe their existence to a large planet 'coming to grief,' but also the comets and meteors, as well as all the rest of the grit and waste which wanders about in our solar system.

Yes, our solar system certainly forms a queer collection. The sun, planets, moons, asteroids, comets and meteors whirl, whizz and revolve past and around one another at enormous speeds and over enormous distances. It would seem to represent a state of chaos, yet almost every movement can be calculated, even that of the comets. Halley was the first to succeed in calculating the path of a comet—and it is to him that we owe the famous 'Halley's Comet.'

The comets are certainly the most spectacular inhabitants of our solar system. Suddenly a magnificent star with a long, shining tail appears in the sky, and no one knows how it has arrived there. The inhabitants of the earth are afraid of it. Does not a comet foretell all manner of terrible punishments from the sky? There used to be many people who committed suicide on the appearance of a comet. History books are full of disasters, calamities and strange happenings which were ascribed to the appearance of comets. This is all now a thing of the past. We now know that comets are honest citizens of our solar system who behave well according to the known rules. They have merely been very fortunate and clearly show it.

We have used the past tense, but must not forget that there were still people during the last appearance of Halley's comet who were firmly convinced that mankind would perish. The earth would float through the tail of the comet and the hydrogen cyanide in that tail would destroy all life on the earth. That was in 1910. At present we know better, and there is no reason whatever for fear. A comet is a quantity of extremely rarefied matter, dust, stones, pieces of ice, frozen gases which together form the 'head' which we see as the 'star.' The heads of comets pass through the solar system on their long journey round the sun in orbits which have the form of more or less flattened ellipses. There are those which roam about within the orbits of the planets, but most of them pass to milliards of kilometres beyond the orbit of Pluto, turn round somewhere there and again move towards the sun. Curving round the sun, the comet turns around and starts its journey all over again. The orbit may be so long that a comet needs hundreds of thousands of years for one revolution, but there are also comets which require only a few years for one journey. The head of the comet—and that is the real comet—is invisible until it reaches the neighbourhood of the sun, for only there does it receive sufficient light to become visible and sufficient heat to form a tail. The gases and the extremely small particles of matter present in the head thaw out and become vaporized in the heat of the sun and then the pressure of the sun's light forces them out of the head. The radiation of light exerts a certain pressure on extremely small particles such as molecules of gas and even on very small pieces of matter. The light coming from the sun forces matter out of

48

the head of the comet and that matter forms the tail which when illuminated by the sun can sometimes create such an impressive effect. This process also explains why the tail is directed away from the sun.

Sometimes a tail can have a very respectable length. Halley's comet could in 1910 boast of a tail 150 million kilometres in length, that is the average distance between the earth and the sun! Yet a comet does not contain as much matter as we are inclined to believe. On an average its density is no more than a quarter of a millionth part of that of the air surrounding the earth. Sometimes it is even so small that there is less matter in the thousand cubic kilometres of space taken up by the comet than in one cubic centimetre of air.

No, comets cannot do any harm. Even a frontal collision between the head of a comet and the earth would scarcely harm us. The greater part of the head would vaporize in the atmosphere and the large fragments would drive into the earth. Their effect would be that of a bombardment during the war, which, terrible as it might have been, left the earth unscarred as a planet.

This is just as well too. Professor Oort has calculated that a 'cloud' of about 100 milliard heads of comets stretches around our solar system. They would certainly not all come in the direction of the earth at the same time, but a small part of them is still an appreciable number.

In any case not very many comets have been observed. We know only of a few thousand. This means that we could be confronted suddenly with a surprise any moment on any evening, at one moment there being nothing to be seen and suddenly a comet appearing in its full magnificence in the sky. Such a sudden appearance is naturally much more interesting and romantic for an inhabitant of the earth than one which has been calculated by astronomers on the basis of previous passages around the sun. This, in many cases, involves a calculation which is amongst the most difficult in the whole of astronomy.

For those who feel that it is a pity that even comets can be calculated, it may be a consolation that poetry has not been completely lost, since there are in our solar system also phenomena which cannot be captured in the dry figures of mathematical formulae. These are the meteors or 'shooting stars.' Astronomers can of course say on what nights of the year and from what directions many shooting stars—which are in any case not stars at all—will be able to be seen, but nothing at all can be calculated about the individual meteors.

Astronomers do not worry very much about them either. Meteors are, when all is said and done, nothing but the waste in our solar system. They are pieces of stone and iron which float about aimlessly through interplanetary space until the force of gravity of the earth seizes them. Their dimensions can vary from those of a piece of dust to those of fragments of matter weighing several tons. When the force of gravity seizes such a meteor, it is forced in the direction of the earth. It penetrates into the atmosphere at a very high speed. Even at a great height the friction of the air becomes so great that the meteor becomes hot, begins to glow and emits light. It has then become a 'shooting star' or meteorite. Leaving a shining trace across the dark sky, the meteor becomes so hot that it vaporizes. A star has been 'shot' at the earth, and those who have seen it may wish . . .

Most meteors are so small that they vaporize completely before they can reach the earth's surface. There are however also larger pieces amongst them which certainly become hot, but which cannot vaporize completely. Such meteorites drive into the earth. Somewhere in South-West Africa there is a piece weighing about 60 tons in the ground. And in Siberia there is said to be one—it cannot be found since it drove deeply into the ground—which must be even heavier. This piece struck the earth on 30th June, 1908, with unimaginable force, destroying 1,200 square kilometres of forest. It was very fortunate that this meteorite descended in an uninhabited region. Meteorites of this size are extremely rare. Most of them are very much smaller and descend without causing any damage. The oceans which cover two-thirds of the earth's surface receive the lion's share of meteorites, the total weight of which amounts to several hundred tons every year.

Meteors are consequently in some respects dangerous. The word 'dangerous' must however be taken with a large grain of salt, for the chance of a meteorite of any size falling in an inhabited area is no greater than one in a few million. No cases are known of people having been killed by meteorites.

Meteors and comets are very different phenomena, but they are much more closely related than one would at first sight imagine. Where do the dust and 'wandering stones' which descend as meteorites come from? We have called them 'waste,' but waste from what?

The Italian astronomer Schiaparelli once again started calculating and discovered that the orbit of certain groups of fragments in space agreed approximately with that of certain comets. In fact meteors are for the most part remains of comets, dust which has been left behind by comets in their orbits. When the earth passes one of these cometary orbits, very many of these remains come within its force of gravity—with fatal consequences for them. Then we see a shower of shooting stars on the earth. The earth also collects waste outside the orbits of comets, since this is present throughout the solar system. It has been estimated that the earth collects 24 million fragments of this type every twenty-four hours.

Planets, moons, asteroids, comets, meteors, all these are kept under control and ruled by the master of our solar system, the sun, that enormous glowing ball of gas whose acquaintance we must now make. What a force must proceed from this mass of gas and what a predominant place the sun must occupy in the order of creation! Yes, indeed—according to our standards— the influence and importance of the sun is enormous. But in the universe we must not use our standards for determining the place of the sun in the whole cosmos, since in that whole the sun is nothing but a very ordinary, insignificant star of the umpteenth order, in other words a small amount of gas of which there are milliards and milliards.

It may well be imagined that the sun is large. Just how large appears only from a few figures and these are so immense that they almost exceed the power of human imagination. No, it takes some effort for us to imagine what the sun is, but let us try.

The diameter of the sun is more than 100 times that of the earth, namely 1,390,000 kilometres. This means that its volume is about 1·3 million times larger than that of the earth. Since however the density of the sun is less than that of the earth, the

51

sun's mass is 'only' 332,000 times as great as that of the earth. Of all the matter of which our whole solar system consists 97-98% is concentrated in the sun. All the planets, moons and the rest together form only 2-3% of the matter in our solar system!

All this enormous ball we call the sun consists of glowing gases, with a surface temperature of about 6,000° and at its centre at temperatures of not less than about 20 million degrees centigrade. The sun radiates an enormous amount of heat and light. All life on the earth owes its existence to it. The sun gives us heat, food, clothing, fuel, everything. Yet the earth does not even receive a two-milliardth part of the energy which the sun radiates in all directions of the universe. The riddle as to where the sun gets all this energy from was solved not so very long ago. Later we will discuss this solution in detail—here we will merely cautiously mention the words 'nuclear fusion.'

An unimaginably large sphere of glowing gases in which every minute millions of tons of matter are transformed into energy, which keeps planets in their orbits milliards of kilometres away, which has been doing this for thousands of millions of years and which will be able to continue doing so for many milliards of years—that is our sun, a modest little star amongst the billions of stars in the universe. That little star passes through space at a speed of hundreds of metres a second, taking its whole retinue of vassals with it. On one of those vassals, on a piece of dust, which sinks into insignificance beside the sun, we live.

Human understanding is not wide enough to be able to grasp all this. What do we understand of the distances in the solar system, of the amounts of matter, of space, of the dimensions?

Let us again use an aid we have applied before, namely that of proportional reduction. Professor G. van den Bergh has preceded us in this in his book *The Earth and World in Space and Time*. His example is so striking that we cannot do better than quote it:

'Let us take the sun as a sphere with a diameter of 1 metre. Then Mercury becomes a pea at a distance of 40 metres, Venus a cherry 75 metres from the sun, the Earth a cherry about 100 metres away, Mars a large pea 165 metres away, Jupiter an orange 580 metres from the sun, Saturn a small orange 1,100 metres away, Uranus a plum 2,100 metres away, Neptune a plum 3,300 metres from the sun and Pluto a large pea about 4,500 metres away. Even from this we see the almost terrifying emptiness of the Universe. Almost everywhere there is nothing, only here and there an insignificant body wanders about, almost lost in space. There would not be any space on earth for the closest star in this model. We would have to place it, in order to keep the same scale, at a distance of 30,000 kilometres from our sun with its diameter of 1 metre.'

This then is the appearance of our solar system as it stands. We shall, let us say, within a foreseeable period, begin space travel in it, with or without manned vessels. We shall have more to say about space travel later, but it should be said here in advance that with the technical means at present at our disposal we shall not get farther than the moon, Venus and Mars. Unmanned vessels will perhaps be able to reach other planets. For journeys beyond the solar system we shall have to resort to techniques which we do not as yet possess, even if we are ever to possess them. Man is small and his means are very limited. What is wrong with admitting this plainly?

Although we cannot go there in person, we have now made the acquaintance of the whole of our solar system in our mind. It has dimensions which exceed our understanding. And it will become worse. When we penetrate to the world of the stars, we shall find that according to the scale which has to be applied there our solar system with its diameter of milliards of kilometres will have to be viewed as an infinitely small point in world space, a point without dimensions, equivalent to nothing, much as a speck of dust which dances through the room in a ray of the sun is also equivalent to nothing.

Let us therefore be very careful when we speak about space travel and the like. Experts know what they mean by the word space travel, namely reconnoitring the space between the earth and the nearest planets, a space which is negligibly small in the universe. People who are not experts, politicians for example, will have to accept this limitation. Perhaps delegates to the United Nations will then make themselves look ridiculous less often than they do at present when they hold conferences about the consequences of the 'conquest of the universe,' without knowing what they are really talking about! For the conquest of the universe—that is something quite different.

CHAPTER VI

If you can actually recognize the outlines of a bear in the constellation Ursus Major without any trouble, then you deserve a Nobel Prize for your powers of imagination. The stars which collectively form this constellation resemble nothing but stars forming a constellation. The same holds for all the other constellations. Let us, nevertheless, be grateful that the ancient races had a different opinion—they took care that we have a little poetry in otherwise so sober a science as astronomy.

The reason why they thought up names for all types of groups of stars is that they assumed that the stars in these groups did in fact belong together. They took it that all fixed stars—the name confirms it—were fixed firmly on the heavenly vault at the same distance from the earth.

We now know that there can be no question of a fixed heavenly vault and that the stars move in space freely and independently of one another. Constellations are purely chance configurations which in a few centuries will no longer exist or will look quite different. Since the stars are so far away from us, we cannot see that they all move in relation to one another, often at very high speeds. Only after many years, in most cases centuries, can we measure a shift in the relative position of stars.

If somewhere in the country we see a high poplar 50 metres away and almost 3 kilometres behind it the tower of the village church, we should never think of saying that the poplar and the tower belong together merely because they are quite by chance at the place where we are standing projected next to one another on our retina. We know that the image will be quite different if we move a few paces to the left or to the right.

54

The Ancients were not aware that a chance perspective played tricks on them. We are quite aware of this. Why then do we keep these names and continue to use them? Because they are so easy when finding our way about in the sky. For astronomers the names of the constellations have the same significance as the names of the streets in a city for the postman. Say to an astronomer 'Alpha Centauri' and he will immediately know where to look amongst the hundreds of stars.

We mentioned 'Alpha Centauri' deliberately, for the star Alpha (α) in the constellation Centaurus is the sun's nearest neighbour, being the closest bright star. Its distance away amounts only to 40 billion kilometres (a billion is a million million!) and that is a trifle in the universe. We cannot however form any idea of this distance. The number itself, namely 40,000,000,000,000 is unmanageable when calculating. Astronomers have also introduced a larger unit which makes calculations somewhat simpler. Instead of terrestrial kilometres, which have no significance in the universe, they calculate in light years, these being units of approximately 10 billion kilometres. A light year is the distance which light can travel in one year; it is consequently a unit of length and not a unit of time, as might perhaps be imagined. Calculated in this unit of length the star α in Centaurus is 4·2 units away. This is much simpler from the point of view of a calculation, 4·2 instead of a four followed by thirteen noughts. Yet nature makes it even more difficult for us by confronting us with distances of millions of light years. Astronomers do not, however, wish to work with astronomical numbers. When nature appeared with millions of light years, they promptly introduced an even larger unit of distance, the megaparsec, which is about three-and-a-quarter million light years in length, that is to say about 32,000,000,000,000,000,000 kilometres. And for the time being this unit seems to be adequate!

For α Centauri the 'modest' light years are however sufficient, for the 4·2 light years which separate us from this star represent a very small distance, much smaller than the average distance between the stars themselves, this being 30–40 light years. The position in stellar space is just as in interplanetary space; there is very much more space than matter. To each unit of matter there are millions of units of nothing.

How many stars can we see in the sky? Children in particular often ask this when they see all the little lights sparkling through the window when they go to bed. And if father and mother answer: a million, then they ask sleepily whether that is almost as many as a thousand.

The correct answer would disappoint father and mother. With the naked eye we can see, on an average, between three and four hundred stars, providing we have good eyes and the field of view is not restricted by houses, trees or the like.

With a telescope it is quite different. Even with an ordinary pair of opera-glasses we see stars appear at points where they cannot be seen with the naked eye. If one sits at a modern telescope a great shock is in store. We are surrounded by the twinkling of stars, hundreds almost everywhere in the sky. It is a muddle of which we can make neither head nor tail.

Yet there is no question of chaos. All those millions of stars, at tens of billions of kilometres from one another, collectively form a whole. If we look up at the sky on a clear, moonless night, we shall see that whole as a light streak through the black of the sky. The Ancients had a fine name for it, the Milky Way. Naturally the Milky Way is not a road. It is a cluster of stars or galaxy. The galaxy is that system of stars to which belong all those we can see, either with the naked eye or with a telescope. Our sun also forms part of it.

This system is not something imaginary like the constellations. It is a real whole, and during the last few decades much work has been done to find out more about it. It has been calculated that the galaxy contains between 100 and 200 milliard stars and that it is thicker at its centre than at the edges, more or less with the form of a flat disc, which is virtually circular. It is something like two saucepan lids which have been laid together on their hollow edges. The dimensions of the disc have also been calculated. The maximum length is said to be about 100,000 light years and the 'thickness' at the centre between 7,000 and 10,000 light years. Where is our sun in this system? Do not think that it resides as a prince amongst the stars at the heart of the disc. Our sun is about 15 light years from the edge of the disc, that is to say somewhere on the outer edge. If it did not exist—and we too therefore did not exist—it would make no difference to the whole of the galaxy.

What does one shining point mean amongst more than 100 milliard?

The position of the sun also explains the light band in the sky which we call the Milky Way. If we place the saucepan lids in front of us so that the disc lies horizontally, and from a point near the edge, that is where the lids begin to approach one another closely, draw a horizontal line, this appears to pass through the heart and over virtually the whole length of the disc and therefore lies completely inside the lids. That is the direction we follow if we look at the light band in the sky. We find there the heart of the disc, of our galaxy, and the light band is formed by the light of millions and millions of stars which are so far away that they are not seen as separate shining points. If however we draw a vertical line from the point inside our lids, then we come almost directly outside the lids. That is the direction if we look in the sky, as far as possible away from the Milky Way, for example, if we look just above the horizon, while the Milky Way stands vertically above us. There are stars there as well, but far fewer, since the disc is very thin there.

The whole of that galaxy rotates round its centre. Just as all the planets describe orbits around the sun, all the stars describe orbits round the centre of the galaxy. There is however one large difference. The planets encircle one given body, the stars describe orbits around one another, that is to say the stars which lie nearer the outside describe paths around their brothers and sisters in the heart of the family circle and which themselves revolve in turn around the centre. Our sun moves with them. It takes 200 million years to describe one complete orbit around the heart of the galaxy. Bearing in mind the dimensions, this is quite short, but its speed is 300 kilometres per second.

Between 100 and 200 milliard stars. This is an estimate, for we cannot by any means see all the stars. With the most powerful telescope we have we cannot see more than a few per cent of the total population of our galaxy. This is however sufficient to give us an idea of the rich variety of stars which exists. There are very large and very small stars, those which shine powerfully, those which shine faintly, young and old, dense and rarefied stars. There are red stars, white, yellow and blue stars. Each type has its own peculiarities and properties. A red giant is quite different from a white dwarf. Just to give one example, there are stars which are more rarefied than the air of our atmosphere and there are stars in which the matter is so densely packed together that one cubic centimetre would weigh a few tons if brought under the same conditions on to the earth.

Much is already known about the life and character of the individual types of stars. Much more is still unknown. Astronomers do not need to look for work as yet. A large amount of scientific work will, for example, have to be carried out before we can explain satisfactorily the phenomenon of the nova. A nova is a star which suddenly flares up brightly and emits a hundred thousand times as much light as it previously did, after which it gradually returns to its original state. A nova is far exceeded by the supernova which can increase to millions of times its previous intensity of light and then emit more light than all the stars of the galaxy put together. No one knows precisely what this is. It is clear that the stars in question explode with a force which is beyond all powers of imagination. It is likely that certain atomic nuclear processes are responsible for it.

Could the star which we call our sun also play such tricks? According to certain theories there is no reason to suppose that it could not. Others say that our sun does not belong to the very special type of stars which can show this phenomenon and that it cannot consequently explode. Whatever the position may be, we do not really need to worry, for the chance that it will happen is negligibly small and if it were to happen, we should not notice it. If the sun were to become a supernova, then all the planets would vaporize completely in such a short time that we should have no chance to realize what had happened. From one second to the next the earth with all its love and sorrow, war and peace, happiness and misery would go up in smoke. Let us therefore not worry about it and continue to look at the normal stars.

What we on the earth call the size of a star has nothing to do with its dimensions. This size refers merely to the amount of light which we receive from the star. A very bright star does not necessarily have to be large. It may be a small star with a high degree of luminosity or one which is not so very far away. A weak star may well be a very large one which is a long way away or which emits a small amount of light only. None the less astronomers have succeeded in forming a picture of the actual dimensions and properties of several hundred stars. For this they have used all sorts of cunningly devised instruments and have discovered a rich variety in the unity of the galaxy. The extremes lie far apart.

Let us consider the amount of light which is radiated by the stars. The most powerful star which we know emits 400 milliard times as much light as the weakest. The weakest is Van Biesbroek's Star. Our sun radiates 1,300,000 times as much light as it does. The most powerful is S. Doradus which emits 280,000 times as much light as our sun. It should be remembered here that all life on earth would become impossible if the sun were to double its radiation.

Let us have another look at the dimensions. The smallest star which we know so far is one in the constellation Draco and is eight times smaller than our earth. One of the very largest is Epsilon Aurigae, which has a diameter which is 2,000 times that of our sun. How large this is can be imagined if we consider Epsilon Aurigae to be standing where our sun is. The surface of the star would then reach past the orbit of Saturn. In other words, the orbits of Mercury, Venus, Earth, Mars, the asteroids, Jupiter and Saturn would come within the body of the star!

These are extremes. By far the majority of the stars has an average luminosity and average dimensions which do not differ all that much from those of our sun. Our sun belongs to the mass of mediocrity, it is a fashionable star which is not distinguished by any eccentricity from other fashionable stars and goes calmly on its way.

Nothing eccentric? Not so very long ago there were different views on this. After all, our sun has a planetary system and on one of those planets, perhaps even on two, there is the strange phenomenon of 'life'—and that must certainly have been something unique.

We humans are, however, only too ready to view ourselves as the centre of the universe around which everything revolves. In our heart of hearts we find it very attractive to be able to think that we are the only beings in the universe gifted with intelligence and feeling. But must this necessarily be so? If we are honest, we must immediately answer: No. There is no single reason to assume that there should be amongst the milliards and milliards of stars merely one very ordinary average sphere of gas which takes a planetary system with it on the long path from beginning to end. There is even less reason to suppose that, if there are other stars with planetary systems, precisely that one system of our sun should be the only one to harbour 'life.'

We earthly mortals must reconcile ourselves to the thought that we are in no way the centre of the universe, that we are not even anything special. Let me repeat again: if our whole solar system, which is to us so enormously large, were to perish suddenly, it would not make any difference to things in the universe. A little way farther on in the galaxy it would not even be noticed. And that system is, as we will see, but a very small part of the universe!

We must give up the idea that the earth is unique. It appears possible in nature for a sun to carry along planets with it and that 'life' exists on planets. Bearing in mind that our galaxy alone has between 100 and 200 milliard stars, then we must consider the probability very great that the possibility offered by nature has been realized more than once. Assuming the chance of the formation of a planetary system as being very small, something like one in so many million, then this would still mean that there are hundreds of thousands of planetary systems, and in the opinion of many astronomers this chance must be rated much higher. There are even scholars who find the formation of planets around a sun as a *normal* phase in its life! A star without planets would therefore be rarer than one with them.

We can in any case calmly assume that there are in our galaxy at least a few million stars which rejoice in the possession of planets. And there is a very large chance that 'life' in one form or another occurs at least on certain of those millions of planets.

We must not fall into the other extreme and assert that somewhere in the universe, hundreds of light years away, beings walk about on a planet with a body, a head, two arms and two legs, who use oxygen for their respiration, who eat brown bread and an egg for breakfast and have a drink in the pub in the evening after work. Life elsewhere in the universe need in no way mean life in the form in which it occurs on the earth. Even on this old familiar earth of ours there are forms of life which we scarcely recognize as 'life.' At other places in the universe, under quite different conditions from here, living creatures may exist which we would in no way recognize as such. They may even be creatures gifted with reason and feeling, who know of mathematics and experience love.

The chance of life is consequently certainly great, but the chance that life elsewhere in the universe would be completely or approximately like that on the earth is, on the other hand, extremely slight. Why should our terrestrial form of life have to be the standard for all the millions of planets? We have now gradually come to realize the modest place our piece of matter occupies in space.

We can therefore direct the stories about beings from space who are said to have landed in 'flying saucers' and to have spoken with the inhabitants of the earth, to the great realm of fancy. The authors themselves have no idea of just how improbable their stories are!

This does not however mean that all reports about 'flying saucers' must be complete nonsense. Just because we must assume that intellectual life exists elsewhere in the universe, life which has perhaps reached a much higher stage of scientific and technical ability than ours has so far, it must be considered possible that representatives of those forms of life indulge in space travel, as we are about to do in the near future. It may well be that those other forms of life are much more suited for space travel than ours ever will be.

We do not, however, need to fear that we shall ever be troubled by living creatures who inhabit the 'flying saucers'— the existence of which has in any case not yet been *proved*—and who may observe us, assuming of course that they have organs which can be compared with our eyes.

Do not be afraid then, for the possibility is very great that our earth would be for them as inhospitable as Jupiter or Saturn for us. The fact that we live here does not by any means imply that they could also exist here. For example, perhaps these creatures would drown in the sea of air which we call our atmosphere, just as we perish in the water of the sea in which fish flourish. Perhaps what we call 'flying saucers' are for them submarines!

'Flying saucers' or not—life will exist elsewhere in the universe. The question which interests us is whether we shall ever be able to prove it, and whether we shall ever be able to make its acquaintance.

We shall probably never be in a position to do so. Of course we must never say 'never,' but if we bear in mind our galaxy, with its milliards of glowing spheres of gas, thousands of milliards of kilometres apart, with here and there a speck of matter on which something lives, then we must recognize that man is aiming very very high in his desire to go and investigate all this personally. Later on we will look at the practical and theoretical possibilities of space travel in the widest sense of the word, but we can calmly state here that we shall never be able to reach more than a very small part of our galaxy. Our form of life is absolutely fixed to the conditions and surroundings in which it arose and in which it will also perish.

A very small part of our galaxy. . . . And that galaxy is by no means the universe. It is negligibly small in the whole universe.

Let us have a further look at the world traveller whom we have already met in the previous chapters. On his way to make a voyage round the world he had arrived at the front door of his house. He had landed on Pluto, the outermost planet of our solar system. Assuming that he could cross the whole of the galaxy and had arrived right through its centre at the outermost border, would he then have almost completed his journey? He would not have advanced farther than the edge of the city in which he lives—he would still have to begin his voyage round the world.

CHAPTER VII

CLUSTERS OF STARS REACH TOWARDS INFINITY. PROFESSOR
OORT SWITCHED ON THE RADIO . . . THE UNIVERSE IS
BECOMING LARGER AND LARGER

Professor J. H. Oort, professor of astronomy at the State University in Leyden, switched on the radio. He listened for a moment and said: 'The galaxy is a spiral nebula.'

No, it was not as simple as that. On the contrary, it was extremely complicated and involved much mathematical effort, technical ingenuity and scientific work of all types before the—cautious—conclusion could be drawn, that the galaxy is not merely a disc-shaped collection of stars, but has a very special structure.

This conclusion became possible in recent years only through the use of the radio telescope, an instrument which was conceived before World War II, but which was not in full use until after 1945.

Up till then scholars knew nothing about the universe other than what the light which comes to us from space could tell them. That was a vast amount—but scholars never consider they know enough. Light is only one of the many types of electromagnetic radiation which exist in nature. It has a very short wavelength. Radiation of a somewhat longer wavelength is called heat and radio waves are even longer. The universe has an ample supply of all types of radiation, but astronomers could only obtain information from light. Radio telescopes have now made it possible to acquire information about conditions in space from radio waves as well. By means of special aerials radio waves from space are collected and are registered by equally special receivers. It seems likely that radio astronomy will be able to provide as yet unsuspected treasures in the way of scientific information and that it may well alter radically current views about the universe.

The harvest resulting from the investigation of the galaxy has already been very rich, for thanks to radio astronomy Professor Oort and his colleagues have been able to measure the rotation of the system directly and have also been able to establish much information concerning its construction.

The galaxy appears to have a spiral form. If it is found, as we have done, that the system as a whole has the form of an approximately circular disc, which is thicker in the centre than at the edges, nothing has yet been said about the way in which the stars are grouped in that disc. It has appeared that they do not wander aimlessly about on their journey around the centre, but meander in extended groups around that centre. Let us take a fan, bend the vanes to the left in such a way that they form quite a large angle with their original position, and lay the whole between two saucepan lids. If we could then also bend the vanes in the direction in which they are pointing, the picture would be even more accurate. This will ruin a fan, but provides in return a good picture of the construction of our galaxy.

Actually we do not need the fan at all. Nature itself shows us genuine spiral nebulae. We need only to look through a very powerful telescope and see—providing we know where to look —spiral nebulae in all their magnificence, for our galaxy is not the only system of stars in the universe. There are milliards of them.

It may be asked why it was so long before astronomers discovered how our galaxy is constructed. The reason is very simple. We ourselves are part of the structure of the system and we therefore see things in a false perspective. Since we live in it ourselves, the galaxy cannot be surveyed by us. There is also the fact that enormous clouds, consisting of gases and particles of dust, impair our view of certain parts of the system, including its centre.

If we move away from a problem, we see it in its correct proportions. This applies to all problems, even to astronomical ones. An observer a long way outside our galaxy would have no trouble in determining its construction, just as we have no trouble in determining the structure of other systems of stars.

No trouble. . . . Astronomers have in fact only known of the existence of spiral and other nebulae as separate and independent systems of stars since the last few decades.

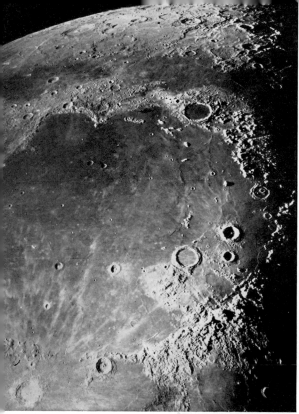

The northern part of the moon, photographed during the last quarter by the huge 100-inch telescope at the American observatory on Mount Wilson. Astronomers prefer to take this type of photograph during the first or last quarter and not, as might be supposed, during full moon when the sun is directly above the part of the moon which is visible to us and the irregularities in its surface, such as craters and mountains, do not cast shadows. During the first or last quarter the sun is low on the moon's horizon, and there is a rich variety of detail because of shadow effects. It is also possible to calculate the height of many objects on the moon from the length of the shadows.

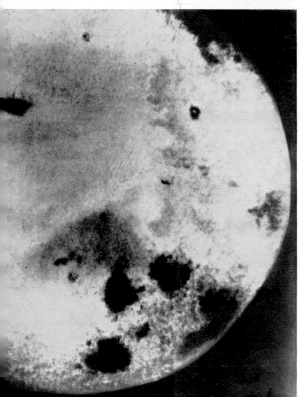

Russian scholars bewildered the world with this photograph. It is the first and, so far, the only photograph of the 'other face' of the moon, which has not yet been seen by human eye. The Russian 'Lunik' which circled the moon took a large number of photographs of the 'other face' and transmitted them to earth by television. Because this photograph was compiled from many negatives American scholars considered it a forgery. They seem to have forgotten that their fellow-countryman, Kuiper, used this same composite method with striking effect on the planet Mars.

This American drawing shows how an eclipse of the sun occurs. The moon stands midway between the sun and the earth and the eclipse is total where the umbra touches the earth. The black band on the earth is the zone of totality. The circular grey region surrounding it experiences a partial eclipse, this being the region where the penumbra touches the earth. Further details are given in Chapter III.

The total eclipse on 30th June, 1954, taken in Minneapolis. The four photographs of the sun were taken during a period of seven minutes. At the bottom left the moon has already covered three-quarters of the sun. Next, the eclipse is already approaching totality and in the centre the sun has disappeared completely. The corona around the moon—not the sun itself, but the hot gases which form its atmosphere—is visible only during eclipses, since under normal circumstances the sun completely outshines it. At the top right the moon has 'released' about a quarter of the sun.

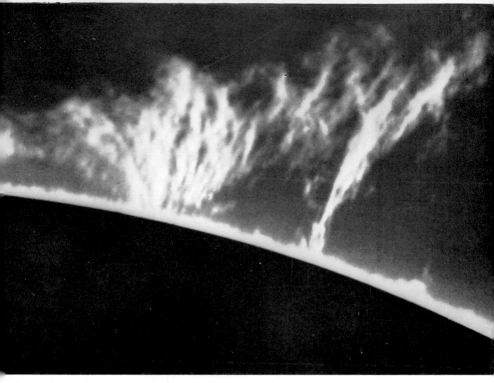

A magnificent solar flame photographed on 21st August, 1909, at Mount Wilson observatory. From time to time enormous jets of glowing gases flare up from the body of the sun, rising to very great heights. This one was no less than 120,000 kilometres high. There is still no clear explanation of this phenomenon.

A brilliant photograph of the sun's atmosphere taken during the total eclipse of 8th June, 1918, in the observatory at Green River, Wyoming.

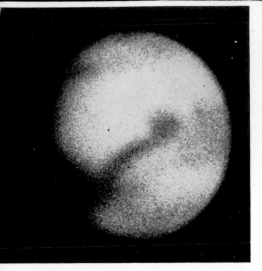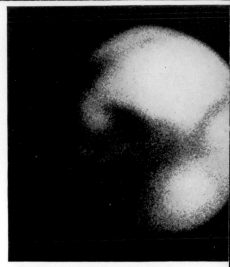

Two photographs of the planet Mars, taken at an interval of a few hours. It can be clearly seen from surface details that the planet has rotated during the interval.

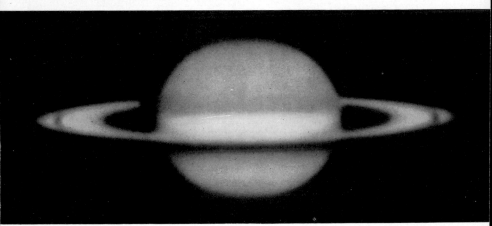

This—it need hardly be said—is Saturn, the planet with the rings. They probably consist of fragments of a former moon which came too close to the planet and was smashed to pieces by the force of gravity. They are a magnificent sight through a telescope.

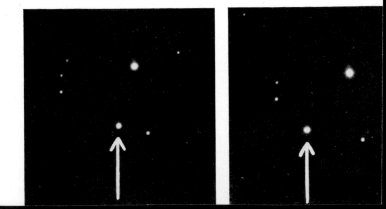

(*Left*) Halley's comet, during its last appearance. The photograph was taken on 12th May, 1910, in Honolulu. The comet was brilliant in the tropics, but in the Northern hemisphere it could be seen only with difficulty as a vague spot in the sky. (*top right*) The Arend–Roland comet, a very recent arrival in the sky, taken on 21st February, 1957, at the powerful Mount Palomar observatory, California. (*bottom right*) The great dome of the Mount Palomar observatory which houses the world's largest telescope. The dome has 10 storeys.

(*Opposite*) How the planet Pluto was discovered. On a photograph resembling the left-hand illustration, the American Clyde Tombaugh discovered a previously unknown point of light (shown by the arrow). It could very well have been a small star which had not previously been observed. But on a later photograph, resembling the right-hand illustration, the small star appeared to have moved slightly in relation to other points of light. Therefore, it could not be a star, it was a planet.

The Milky Way in all its magnificence photographed at Mount Wilson. This is in the constellation Sagittarius.

(*Above*) The world's most powerful telescope, the Hale telescope, in the Mount Palomar observatory. (*below*) Thanks to the 'analysis' of light, astronomers have learnt much about the composition and properties of the stars. Known as spectral analysis, it may well be called the magic book of astrophysics. This spectrogram is of the star α in the constellation Cygnus. From the nature and position of all the lines, it is possible to deduce what elements occur in the star, how it moves, and other information.

The nearest large cluster of stars, equivalent to our Milky Way, is the Andromeda nebula. Under favourable circumstances it can be seen with the naked eye as a very small shining disc in the constellation Andromeda. It is called 'M 31' in the dry language of the astronomical catalogue, in which everything found in the universe is neatly classified. This symbol covers a cluster of stars similar to our own Milky Way. 'M 31' contains between 100 and 200 milliard stars, each milliards and milliards of kilometres apart, but so far from us that we see them as one white spot. The nebula is one-and-a-half million light-years away—a negligible distance in the universe.

Numerous observers had in the course of the years seen with their continually improving instruments at many points in the sky small nebulous points of light as well as the stars. A point of this type could be seen in the constellation Andromeda even with the naked eye. No one suspected the truth. There were those who thought the spots were clouds of gas or dust which were illuminated by a neighbouring star. Others considered that it was a gas which was in the process of contracting to form a star. There were many suppositions which nevertheless all agreed on one point; the spots, whatever they may be, belonged to the galaxy.

Then the huge telescope of the Mount Wilson observatory in America came into use and the astronomer, E. P. Hubble, began the observations which were to win him a great reputation. He was aided by many others, and a whole new picture of the universe was soon formed.

Just as once, a few hundred years ago, the earth had lost its privileged position as the centre of the universe, the galaxy was also deposed from its throne as ruler of the universe. The galaxy was not 'the' universe—it appeared in fact to be such a small part of it that it could disappear with all its milliards of stars without making any difference to the situation in the universe.

Astronomers succeeded in determining the distance between many nebulae. According to the old views these could never amount to more than about 100,000 light years, the largest dimension in our system of stars. But astronomers were confronted with the Andromeda Nebula at a distance of no less than about one-and-a-half million light years—and it is one of the closest! The most distant nebulae which can be detected with the powerful telescopes of the great American observatories are more than *five milliard* light years from the earth. If we wished to express this distance in terrestrial kilometres, we would have to put a row of 22 noughts after the number 5, making fifty thousand trillion.

The large telescopes have revealed the nature of at least the closest nebulae. They did not appear to be clouds of gases or dust, but galaxies. They are systems of stars of the same type as our galaxy, each consisting of milliards of stars, which are in turn some hundreds or thousands of light years away from one another, stars probably with planets, on which there is probably life. They also have the form of a disc and spiral arms around a core. There are however also nebulae which do not have a spiral form, there are spherical ones, and all sorts of other variations. Astronomers tend to assume that all the different forms are phases in the life of a system of stars and that we therefore see systems in all stages of development. There are systems which are accompanied by 'satellite nebulae,' there are accumulations of systems, which clearly belong together in a different way. Thus our galaxy belongs to a group of which the Andromeda Nebula and a few other close, smaller systems form part.

Astronomers have also tried to answer the question as to how many systems of stars there are. The answer is bewildering. In that part of the universe to which our telescopes can penetrate, there are hundreds of millions of systems of stars, of which our system is one. Ours is not the largest and not the smallest—it belongs to the mediocrity, as does our sun amongst the millions of stars of our galaxy.

We can detect hundreds of millions of galaxies with our telescopes, but it is estimated that we can reach only $1 \cdot 5\%$ of the universe with these instruments. Who knows what there is in the remaining $98 \cdot 5\%$ of space into which a terrestrial eye has not yet penetrated?

$1 \cdot 5\%$ of the universe. How can we really speak of 'per cent of space'? Space must after all be infinite, for if it were not, what would be at the spot where space ends? And we cannot determine the contents of an infinite space—the contents are then also infinite? And what does $1 \cdot 5\%$ mean?

A very innocent sentence raises a flood of questions. They are questions to which modern science has an answer, and that answer is: Yes. We can in the opinion of many in fact speak of 'per cent of the universe,' for the universe is not infinite.[1] We can state its contents as a terrestrial number. We can according to some astronomers even estimate its total mass and express it in ordinary kilogrammes. This is however such a comprehensive subject that we will come back to it later in greater detail—we are now discussing the galaxies in the universe, of which there are therefore countless milliards.

[1] Compare Chapter XV regarding this point, where quite a different theory is explained.

66

Once again we can ask an old question: do all these milliards and milliards of systems wander about arbitrarily in space without any fixed plan? And once again we must answer this question in the negative. We can now even go so far as to say that nothing happens in the universe without a fixed plan, everything in creation, be it matter or energy, obeys inexorable laws of nature, which are the same everywhere.

There is consequently no arbitrary movement. But how do the systems move in relation to one another? Hubble's observations were so surprising that astronomers must have looked at one another in amazement. But the facts were there, were confirmed again and again and did not alter, whatever one did with them.

All galaxies appeared to be moving farther away from ours! They were, at a high speed, making the distance between themselves and our system greater. The farther they are away, the greater their speed.

Could our galaxy then occupy a central place in the universe after all? Could our system of stars be the centre of creation, just as the Ancients once considered that the earth was the centre of the universe?

Once again human vanity was to suffer a disappointment. Our galaxy does not behave differently from the others. They are all flying away from one another. To be precise, all *groups* of systems of stars are increasing their distance from one another. For our galaxy and the Andromeda Nebula, which belong to the same group, do not show this phenomenon.

Every second the distances between the groups of galaxies are without exception becoming greater. It is as during an explosion, the fragments fly in all directions and the distances between all the fragments become greater and greater—until the fragments settle somewhere. Galaxies cannot fall—and this is why they recede farther and farther from one another as after an explosion. This is why the universe is continually becoming larger!

According to a number of theories this is also what must have happened. What we see and what we are, is the result of an unimaginably violent explosion which gave birth to the universe at the beginning of time. It should however be said that other theories contest this. It depends whether the correctness of one of the two views will ever be proved. We are in the final analysis human beings, and our powers are extremely limited, bearing in mind the unimaginable magnitudes in the universe. Let us once again introduce the world traveller from the previous chapter before leaving the man to his fate. He was at the end of our galaxy and was standing at the edge of the city in which he lives. Now he has covered a few million light years and is at the outermost border of the group of systems of stars to which our galaxy belongs, the so-called 'local group.' Is he now at the end of his voyage around the world? On the contrary—he is getting his passport out for the first time as he stands at the border of his own country. He is just about to *begin* his voyage around the world!

The fact that we as human beings are, in spite of our reason, but small, helpless creatures in the unfathomable spaces of creation, will also set very close limits to our possibilities of penetrating into those spaces.

Space travel has become a fashionable word before there is any question of space travel. Only very few of those who like to play with this word realize however the few possibilities and the many impossibilities.

There are men of science for whom the question of how far man will be able to remove himself from the earth does not arise at all. They consider that it will be simply impossible for man to leave the earth and hold that the only possible space travel will be the sending of unmanned 'space laboratories' to the moon, Venus, Mars and possibly other not too distant objects. They consider that man on entering space himself would be subjected to phenomena of nature which would be lethal and against which he would not be able to protect himself. Space is full of dangerous cosmic and other radioactive radiation, there are unbearably high and low temperatures, meteors wander about which can cause collisions, and the conditions on other heavenly bodies are so extremely different from those on the earth that man, once having left our planet, is doomed to perish.

Other men of science smile at these arguments and recall that the train and aeroplane were formerly rejected by experts as being dangerous and 'inhuman.' They believe that problems for which no solution can be given at the moment will be removed from the world as science and techniques continue to develop. There will be new machinery, and new materials, new aids, new basic materials and what is now impossible will one day be childishly simple, that is the opinion of these experts.

The pessimists and optimists are therefore diametrically opposed to one another. Who will be right?

It is a question here of drawing a picture of space travel. We do not get far with this by adopting the views of the pessimists. Let us therefore follow the optimists—they are in any case in the majority—and assume that man will one day be able to leave the earth, by which we do *not* mean to say that the optimists are in fact right. The future will give the answer about right or wrong.

Let us therefore assume that the artificial satellites and rockets to the moon of the present will be followed by manned ships to the moon and, at a later stage, to the neighbouring planets, Venus and Mars. Does a landing on Mars mean that man 'has conquered space'? The answer is, No, and does not really need to be said. Let us assume the average distance from the earth to Mars to be 80 million kilometres—what is this distance compared with the one-and-a-half million light years or almost 15 trillion kilometres (fifteen times a million times a million times a million!) which separate us from the Andromeda Nebula, one of the nearest of the milliards of systems?

Let us remain much nearer home, in our own galaxy, and close to our own solar system. In our winter sky is the magnificent star, Sirius, once the holy star of the ancient Egyptians. It is one of the nearest neighbours of the sun—being in fact the fifth nearest and is only 8·8 light years or 82 billion kilometres away from us. Let us assume that man will one day be in a position to cover such a great distance—what does this distance mean in the universe? Of course a journey to a possible planet of Sirius would be real space travel, and by no means a short journey. Would we then 'have conquered space' by such a journey?

The Austrian astronomer, Dr. O. Thomas, will extricate us from our dream. He once investigated the relationships if we imagine the universe as being one thousandth trillionth of its true size. The diameter of the known universe then becomes 10 kilometres. Our galaxy acquires a diameter of 1 metre and the

Andromeda Nebula is 15 metres from it. What is on this scale the distance of 82 billion kilometres between Sirius and us? One-tenth of a *millimetre*—the thickness of the cutting edge of a razor blade!

No, even when we have landed on Sirius's presumed planet we will not have 'conquered' space. And we can calmly state here, in deliberate deviation from the golden rule that one must never say 'never,' that the 'conquering' of the universe by man is eternally impossible.

Why shall we never get that far even if we wanted to? Not because of our technical ability. If the optimists are in fact right and man can one day go to the moon, Mars or Venus, then there is no technical obstruction which would make a journey to the Andromeda Nebula impossible. But the distance plays a trick on us since the distances in the universe are far too great! A journey to the Andromeda Nebula would last many human lives, even if we were to travel almost as fast as nature permits.

For this is the great stumbling-block. Nature has a maximum speed. The speed of the propagation of light in an empty space, which is 299,776 kilometres per second—rounded off for convenience to 300,000 kilometres per second—is at the same time the maximum speed which is possible in the universe, for energy, for matter, for everything. The stories about journeys in space ships which travel many times the speed of light may still be very attractive—they are fairy tales and will always remain so, for nature is inexorable, 300,000 kilometres per second and not a metre more. This makes space as a whole, in which our solar system and even our galaxy are virtually nothing, inaccessible to man.

And here, as is becoming more and more common at present, a few conquerors of the universe raise their fingers to recall a name and a few concepts which have become part and parcel of science.

That name is: Albert Einstein. Those concepts are: the relative slowing down of time and relative contraction of length. We have in fact so far not taken into account the theories of relativity, theories which are at present bandied about in explanations about space travel and from which conclusions are often drawn which are preposterous. If we do consider them, will our conclusions be different?

In the next chapter we will assume not only that space travel will be possible, but that it also will be able to be undertaken in such a way that account will have to be taken of the phenomena of relativity. We will not take this point of departure because it is said to be right, we will do it merely in order to have the opportunity to explain one of the greatest wonders of nature.

CHAPTER VIII

WITH EINSTEIN THROUGH SPACE AND TIME. SPACE AND
TIME ARE RELATIVE. MAN WILL NEVER CONQUER THE
UNIVERSE. LET MANKIND ABOVE ALL REMAIN
LEVEL-HEADED!

The teacher writes a sum on the blackboard. After how long, he writes, will a traveller in space return to the earth if he makes a journey at a speed of 99% of that of light to and from a planet of the star Sirius, which is 8·8 light years away from earth? Two small boys, next to one another on a seat, bend over their paper. When they have finished the sum, they sit up, their arms crossed.

'And, John?'

'He will return after 17 years and 180 days, sir.'

'Good—that is the correct answer. And, Albert?'

'He will return after 2 years and 194 days, sir.'

'Fine—that is the correct answer.'

In 1962 no teacher would think of stating that two totally different answers to the same sum are both correct. He assumes that two and two are always and under all circumstances four. But should the era of interstellar space travel ever dawn, he will then have a more difficult task. He will then have to recognize that two and two by no means always have to be four, and that John and Albert, however different their answers were, have both given the correct answer to his question. He will have to take into account that his pupils have considered the sums about space travel from a different point of view, and that the result will depend on 'from which side you view the matter.'

John and Albert did in fact view the matter from a different side. John calculated after how long those who had remained on the earth would see the astronaut again. Albert, on the other hand, calculated how much time had passed for the astronaut between his departure and arrival, and for this he took into account the theories of relativity—he was not called Albert for nothing, after the great scholar Albert Einstein, the propounder of those theories.

The possible future astronauts may certainly be grateful to Einstein. He prepared man for the extremely strange things which will happen if he sees the chance to travel through space at a speed approaching that of the propagation of light.

The whys and wherefores of the theories of relativity cannot be explained here. We shall have to restrict ourselves to the consequences of those theories and we shall have trouble enough in accepting them. We shall in fact have to renounce the familiar idea that time and space are firm, immutable concepts. Einstein taught that a second does not under all circumstances last just as long and that a metre is not always and everywhere equal to the terrestrial standard of length. Even the amount of matter, the mass of an object, is not immutable.

In a space ship which moves very fast with regard to the earth, time will pass more slowly than on the earth. Not only will the clocks go more slowly, but all scientific and biological processes, such as the vibrations we call light, breathing and thought. A second has a different meaning in that ship from what it has on earth, a different meaning for the observer on the earth, not for the astronaut himself.

In that rapidly moving space ship all dimensions in the direction of movement have also become shorter. A metre is not equal to a terrestrial metre, but may, for example, be half a metre, according to the terrestrial standard. The astronaut, however, who measures it will find precisely one metre.

The mass of the space ship, measured by a terrestrial observer, will no longer be 1,000 kilogrammes but, for example, 2,000 kilogrammes. The astronaut, however, will not find one gramme more than 1,000 kilogrammes if he starts experimenting.

In other words, all these phenomena are *relative*; they occur only for observers who do not have the same speed as the space ship, and the degree to which they occur depends on the speed of the space ship relative to those observers. The men in the space ship will not notice anything, and they cannot, since for them these peculiarities do not occur. On the other hand, they will find that everything is 'normal' for them, but that it is the

73

earth, with all those observers on it, which shows a slowing down of time, a contraction of length and an increase in mass. For they can, as Einstein has taught, say that they are not moving in relation to the earth, but that the earth is moving in relation to them! And since the earth consequently has a high speed relative to the astronauts, the consequences of that speed are shown on the earth.

The question is obvious: yes, but who is in fact really moving? We cannot say that the space ship is moving and is at the same time stationary?

Let us return from space to the earth for a moment. Two passengers are sitting opposite one another in a train. At the end of the journey passenger 'A' will be prepared to swear that passenger 'B' has not left his seat and that he has not moved. A level-crossing keeper, however, who has seen the train passing will be prepared to swear that passenger 'B' has moved with a speed of not less than 120 kilometres per hour, this being the speed of the train. Neither passenger 'A' nor the level-crossing keeper would have committed perjury, for both were correct. Passenger 'B' moved and did not move at one and the same moment. No one will have any difficulty with the explanation of this contradiction. Passenger 'B' was not moving relative to the train in which passenger 'A' was also sitting, but was moving relative to the level-crossing keeper who was not sitting in the train. The train itself was moving relative to the level-crossing keeper, who was stationary.

We must now take a further step which again brings us into space. Was that level-crossing keeper really standing still? No, he was standing on the earth, and it rotates not only round its axis, but also revolves around the sun. If these two movements of the earth were precisely opposed to the direction of the train and could together produce a precisely equally large movement in that opposite direction, what should we be able to say then? It would be obvious to say that the train with the two passengers was stationary relative to the sun, but that the level-crossing keeper was moving relative to the sun. But would the train also be stationary relative, for example, to the star Sirius? No, for the sun moves relative to that star!

This simple example shows that it is never possible to decide what is moving and what is not. Movement in the absolute sense can never be shown. Scientifically it means something only if we speak of movement relative to something else. Einstein concluded that all the laws of nature hold independently of the movement of the system within which they are observed. Only if we perceive those laws in a different system, which is moving relative to the observation post, must we take into account the relative movement. It does not make any difference whether we regard that system or the observation post as moving.

And here we are back in the space ship, moving or not, but in any case at a high speed relative to the earth, and consequently with a different time, a different length and a different mass from what the observers on the earth found when the ship was still safely standing on the ground. Time proceeds more slowly, consequently the passengers become old less quickly than those who have remained behind on the earth, they act more slowly, think more slowly—at least, according to those who remain behind! They themselves go on as usual and for them nothing is different from what it was at home. It takes five minutes to boil an egg and a kilogramme of sugar lasts just as long as on the earth. Before we delve into the practical consequences of these strange phenomena, we would like to ask whether they are really 'genuine.' Einstein propounded all this in his theories of relativity, but those are only *theories*. It is obvious that scientists did everything in their power to show the correctness or otherwise of Einstein's theory. The result of their efforts is that the correctness of the theories of relativity, in so far as they can be tested experimentally, is beyond all doubt. One of the phenomena of relativity, namely the increase in mass, has even become a factor of which account must be taken in a sober technical realm. In modern nuclear physics apparatus is used at present for investigations in which electrically charged atomic particles and atomic nuclei are accelerated to very high speeds. We shall be discussing these cyclotrons later. A relative increase in mass occurs in this apparatus on the part of the accelerated particles and account has to be taken of it in constructing cyclotrons. They are then also called *synchro*trons, because they are *synchronized* for the increase in mass!

The relativity of nature must therefore be accepted as established, even if its consequences are difficult for human logic to digest. To our 'healthy understanding' a second is a second, a metre is a metre and a gramme is a gramme. But what is healthy understanding? According to Einstein 'a collection of prejudices which are fed to us with a porridge spoon before our eighteenth year.' Nature is just as it is, and the limited nature of his powers makes it impossible for man to penetrate it completely. Just as a glow-worm will never be in a position to write a thesis on the Corporate Organization of Industry, man will never be able to 'understand' nature completely.

Perhaps the problems of relativity would not be at all difficult for man if the phenomena were to reveal themselves at speeds with which we are confronted in everyday life. If a car at a speed of 80 kilometres per hour were to be only half as long as when it was at rest, then no one would find this strange. It is incorrect to assume that a moving car is just as long as a stationary one, but at our normal speeds the relative contraction in length is so slight that it cannot be shown in any way.

A calculation shows that a car travelling at 80 kilometres per hour contracts by a fraction of a milliardth part of a centimetre —and only a chronic grumbler would pay attention to that! The phenomena do not become noticeable and measurable until speeds which approach that of the propagation of light are reached, and should man ever be in a position to attain these speeds, then the relativity of nature will very quickly become quite a normal matter. And then too the final word will be spoken in the controversy which divides opinion amongst optimistic astronauts, namely that concerning the actual consequences of space travel at very high speeds.

People are generally agreed that in a space ship which moves at 99% of the speed of light, that is 297,000 kilometres per second, time will pass seven times as slowly as on the earth. The men in the ship will therefore become one year older during the time in which seven years pass on earth.[1] Let us assume that they leave for a journey of fourteen years; fourteen years on the earth we mean—are they on their return two years older while everything and everyone on earth has become fourteen years older? Writers of science fiction have already answered this question unreservedly in the affirmative and have described situations in which a father was younger than his son as a result

[1] A worked out mathematical consideration of this example is included in the Appendix.

of a very long journey in space. Scholars however are by no means agreed on the answer, and this is understandable, for there are in principle three possibilities and heavy arguments for each of them, while no proof has yet been forthcoming for any of them.

The majority of the experts considers that the writers of science fiction are correct. Others, on the other hand, consider that the astronauts will 'lose' just as much on their return journey as they 'gain' on the journey out, so that they will have become just as old as their relatives who remained behind. A third group holds strongly to the relativity of the slowing down of time. These experts say that the slowing down is produced in the ship according to those who stay behind, but also manifests itself on earth according to the astronauts, and to the same extent, so that the clocks keep in time. The only result would be that a journey into space takes much less time than normal calculations would suggest.

Let us look again at the above example. The majority says that the astronaut will be two years older and the earth fourteen years older (John and Albert therefore represent the view of the majority). The second view leads to the conclusion that both the astronaut and the earth will be fourteen years older. The last opinion maintains that the astronaut and the earth will both be two years older than at the time of departure.

This problem, which in science has become known as the 'paradox of the clock,' has many other aspects. There is no point in considering them further here, since we already know enough to be able to answer the question as to whether man, thanks to the relativity of nature, will after all be able to conquer the whole universe, should he ever turn out to be in a position to undertake space travel, this question being answered so willingly in the affirmative by the 'conquerors of the universe.'

Let us in formulating our answer proceed in a proper democratic way from the point of view of the majority that the astronaut will get older less quickly than those who remain on the earth. Let us further join the ranks of the super-optimists who are convinced that man will one day succeed in thinking out a method of propulsion which will make the necessary speeds possible. These super-optimists like to play with the thought of a photon rocket, that is a rocket which is propelled

77

by the pressure of the radiation of light, the same pressure which provides the comets with their tails. What such a ship would look like, no mortal yet knows. And even if it is already possible in theory—no expert would dare to say anything about how it could be carried out in practice.

Be this as it may—we start with John and Albert's sum about the journey to Sirius and find that the traveller, having become two years older, returns to the earth seventeen years after his departure. He has travelled at a speed of 297,000 kilometres per second, that is 99% of the speed of light.

It is essential that the man should be away from the earth for seventeen years; space travel will be engaged in for scientific purposes and only has any meaning if its results are made known on earth. Scholars on the earth will therefore have to wait seventeen years for the data which the traveller to Sirius has collected, for radio cannot help either him or the earth! Radio signals have, in common with light, a speed of propagation of 300,000 kilometres a second. If the astronaut, half-way to Sirius, that is at 4·4 light years away, sends a message to the earth, his signal will not reach the earth until 4·4 years after it is sent. In those 4·4 years the traveller will have just arrived on Sirius. Assuming that he turns round immediately and that the earth answers immediately, then the signal from the earth will reach the traveller when he is again at the spot from where he sent the signal. If the astronaut makes important observations on Sirius, which he straight away signals to the earth and then starts on the return journey himself, then he will land on the earth just after his observations have been received. He will be travelling after the radio signal with a difference in speed of only 1%.

A journey to Sirius therefore means for the astronaut about two years of solitary confinement and for the earth seventeen years of impatient waiting. But what is a journey to Sirius compared with the size of the universe? One-tenth of a millimetre in a total of 10 kilometres!

A tenth of a millimetre—seventeen years. And even then the speed of the traveller is 99% of that of light. If it is desired in the same way to look at the centre of our galaxy, then a journey of about 69,000 years will be necessary—in the terrestrial sense. But the traveller has the advantage of the slowing down of time?

78

True, but for him the journey would still last for more than 9,000 years. Before he had completed a hundredth part of his journey his life would be at an end. A visit to the centre of the galaxy is therefore impossible, even at 99% of the speed of light.

Yet there is still a possibility. We are in the final analysis not limited to that 99%. If we make it 100 or 300 or 1,000? Here, however, Einstein raises a finger in reprimand. He has shown that the speed of propagation of electromagnetic effects, such as rays of light, radio waves and the like, is at the same time the maximum speed which is possible in nature. And that speed is reserved for those effects alone, everything else in nature has to remain below it, even if it is only a millionth of a millionth per cent. This is certainly understandable. After all, as the speed of an object approaches that of light, time is slowed down, length is contracted and mass is increased. At the moment when the object would reach the speed of light, its time would be stationary, its length would be reduced to zero and its mass would be infinitely large.

We shall never, therefore, reach the speed of light. But what would happen if we could get to 99·99999999%, that is a hundred millionth per cent below the speed of light, 3 centimetres per second slower than light?

It would make little difference to the earth—for it the speed of the traveller to Sirius has not even increased by one full per cent, and the time between departure and arrival therefore remains round about seventeen years. For the traveller himself the difference is however enormous; he will have travelled to and from Sirius in one day. He will breakfast at home, have a cup of coffee on Sirius's planet and be back at home in time for his evening meal. Only—his food would in the meantime have become cold. In about seventeen terrestrial years the traveller will have become twelve hours older. At this speed time in the space ship passes 70,000 times more slowly than on the earth.

This difference is of great importance to the traveller, for apart from Sirius he can now also travel to the centre of the galaxy and if he wishes to the Andromeda Nebula. He will return after one year from his journey to the centre of our galaxy. On his return from the Andromeda Nebula he will have been in solitary confinement for twenty-eight years. But on the earth. . . . Returning from the centre of our galaxy the traveller will find that the earth has advanced 69,000 years further in its history. And when he returns from the Andromeda Nebula he will find an unrecognizable earth, for 3 million years will have passed. And then it will be a depressing thought for him that the Andromeda Nebula is one of the nearest. The distance there is 'merely' one-and-a-half million light years—and galaxies are at present known a few *milliards* of light years away!

Space travel does not mean anything in this way. What is the use to science of an expedition from whom the results will be obtained only after 69,000 years, or after 3 million years? Let it be repeated, space travel, if it is ever possible, will be carried out for the benefit of the knowledge of mankind and not for the —in any case very doubtful—pleasure of the astronaut himself. No government, scientific organization or any other body will make available such enormous amounts as will be necessary for this type of space travel for experiments whose results will never be known to mankind. And in particular, no one will ever wish or be permitted to sacrifice human lives so senselessly for this type of space travel.

Let us, in answering the 'extremists,' go a little farther and assume for a moment that there is no question of the use, costs or human lives, but merely of the *possibility* of penetrating to the farthest parts of the universe. Then we must say that this possibility does not exist, because the same phenomena of relativity which make distant journeys possible limit us on technical grounds, for the increase in mass plays a part. The mass increases as the speed increases. At 99·99999999% of the speed of light the mass is 70,000 times as large as at rest. This means that a space ship weighing 100 tons would have a mass of 7 million tons at that speed. Energy would therefore have to be taken to accelerate a mass of 100 tons which gradually increases to 7 million tons. That amount of energy is enormously large. Somewhere there must be a limit to which speed can be increased with the help of the not unlimited amount of energy which the space traveller can take with him. Let us just assume that this limit is precisely 99·99999999% and that an astronaut can in fact travel to and from the Andromeda Nebula in twenty-eight years. How long would he then require for a return journey to a galaxy 2 milliard light years away? More than 36,000 years! By the way, somewhat more than 4 terrestrial milliard years would have passed in the meantime.

We have by this at the same time proved that, even if the 'relativists' are correct, and the clocks on the earth and in the space ship are slowed down, but at the same rate—we mentioned this as the third possibility—'conquering' the universe is impossible. After all, for a journey to a galaxy 2 milliard light years away—which is really not the most distant—not 4 milliard years would have passed on earth, but 'only' 36,000 years, just as in the space ship. This does not make any difference in practice, since man cannot become tens of thousands of years old.

Apart from all this, man must above all not forget that the universe is every second becoming larger at a speed which approaches that of light!

The question as to whether man can conquer the universe must therefore definitely be answered in the negative. Even if the most optimistic expectations concerning the possibility of space travel turn out to be true, it will always be limited to our solar system and its, astronomically speaking, closest surroundings.

Our form of life arose on the earth and will one day perish with it. Let mankind remain level-headed and try to make life on earth as good as possible for everyone!

CHAPTER IX

EINSTEIN AND THE OLD ENVELOPE. SPACE IS CURVED AND
VIRTUALLY EMPTY. TIME AND SPACE ARE ONE. A JOURNEY
ON A RAY OF LIGHT LEADS US AROUND THE UNIVERSE

Mrs. Einstein, so a story goes, once visited one of the great American observatories. It was explained to her in detail what all the large and small telescopes and all the pieces of complicated auxiliary apparatus were used for. When that had been made clear to her, she looked at her guides and said: 'Do you need all those complicated and expensive things for that? My husband just works out those things on the back of an old envelope.' This was very complimentary to the great physicist, but just as incorrect. Mrs. Einstein was not an objective observer.

Those who practise the exact sciences are in fact objective observers. They watch nature in all its behaviour and set down their findings in mathematical formulae. And they work with these objective data. If they can reconcile the importance and the consequences of their observations and calculations with their imaginative faculty, they naturally find this pleasant. If they cannot do that, however, it is unpleasant for general human vanity—but the objective data do not alter any more than the scientists do. They calculate mathematically with what is inconceivable in the same way as with the most common things. They do not worry whether what they find or consider they find is 'logical' and 'understandable' and 'possible.' We shall have to follow them on their path.

When Einstein, for example, states on the basis of mathematical theories the thesis that the space which we call the universe is curved and when observers in observatories find facts which confirm this, then we shall have to accept that we live in a curved space, whatever that may mean. We shall even have to bow our heads humbly when there is added on top of this that space is curved in the fourth dimension, which exists alongside length, breadth and height and that we may consider time as the fourth dimension.

Fine—we cannot imagine any 'curved space,' but is this then quite inconceivable or illogical? Certainly not. If we take a bit of trouble, we can see what scientists mean by it. Let us then play a little game. We shall be in good company, for Einstein did it often too.

We will go to the sun and climb there on to a ray of light which is just leaving our star. The ray takes us into space at the speed of about 300,000 kilometres per second. For years, centuries, hundreds of centuries we race through the universe in a straight line away from the sun. Naturally in a straight line, since a ray of light always follows the shortest path and does not need to go round any corners in space. How could it anyway? Sitting on our ray we just hope that there will not be any matter in our path, a sun, a particle of dust, for then that would be the end of our ray. We are lucky. For millions and milliards of years we race forward unhindered. To the left and right, above and below us, behind and in front of us we see suns and galaxies shooting past us. We begin to feel ill at ease. How far we are from home, we have left the sun behind us for ever. But strangely enough we suddenly imagine we recognize the surroundings. Have we been here before? We are approaching a point of light, the umpteenth sun. Nine small spheres are revolving around it. It is our own sun, our own solar system— we are home again!

Travelling for millions and milliards of years in a straight line we have returned to our point of departure. We realize what has happened, we have made a journey round the universe!

Here is another game for our thoughts.

Let us imagine that the earth has no oceans and is completely flat. A road begins in London, a beautiful wide motorway. It stretches out to the south-west completely smooth and perfectly horizontal. We drive along the road. We drive for days and days, for weeks and weeks, all the time straight ahead, for there is not a single curve, however slight. What a long way we are from London, 40,000 kilometres in fact! There is a board. On it we read Clapham Junction. What? Yes, we are home again. Merely by driving in a straight line, we have returned to our starting-point.

If we view both these experiences together, is there any difference in principle?

Of course! The road we followed on the earth was not a straight road, it followed the curvature of the earth's surface. If we had thought of that during the ride, we could have carried out measurements to see whether there was any curvature or not. If we had carried out those measurements over a few tens of metres, we should not have been able to find any trace of curvature. And yet it was there, otherwise we should never have been able to return to our point of departure, merely by travelling straight ahead. We should have had to carry out measurements not over a few tens of metres, but over a few tens of kilometres. Then our results would have been different!

Therefore, the one case does not differ in principle from the other? Or would we on our ray of light. . . .

This is in fact so. There is in principle no difference between the two journeys. In the terrestrial case, a two-dimensional road—a road with only length and breadth—curved in the third dimension, in the 'heavenly' case a three-dimensional space—with length, breadth and height—curved in the fourth dimension. It is therefore a difference in degree. The car no more followed a 'straight' path than the light ray did. The ray of light followed the curvature of space in the same way as the car followed the curvature of the earth's surface. On the earth we could not find any trace of curvature over a short distance of the road, so that we could consider that piece as absolutely straight. The same is true of the universe. We can with our limited aids measure only a small part of total space, and that section is too small to show the curvature clearly. But that curvature exists nevertheless. Astronomers seem with their latest aids to be well on the way to making measurements which will provide clear results.

Yes, but how can we imagine a space which is curved in the fourth dimension? And what does it mean by saying that we should consider time as that fourth dimension? Dimensions are perpendicular to one another. Length is perpendicular to breadth and height, breadth to length and height and height to length and breadth. And is time now to stand perpendicular to length and breadth and height? What nonsense is this?

At first sight it does in fact seem nonsense, but on closer

observation it becomes clearer. What do scientists mean when they talk about the curvature of space?

The curvature of space is nothing more than a mathematical concept. Everyone knows that the sum of the three angles of a triangle which we draw on a piece of paper amounts to 180 degrees. Whatever triangle we think up, the sum of the three angles is always 180 degrees. At least if it is a *flat* triangle. For a triangle drawn on a sphere is different. Let us take two points on the equator which are a quarter of the circumference of the globe apart, and draw lines from there to the North Pole. That triangle does not consist of straight lines, but of curved lines. And the sum of the three angles is 270 degrees! This is due to the fact that the surface of the triangle is *curved*. And now to space. When astronomers started experimenting after the publication of Einstein's theories, they discovered that triangles in space, for example between the earth and two stars, had the same properties as those on a globe and that they were not equal to those on a flat plane. And they concluded that space is therefore curved! In other words, there is no point in imagining a curved space, any more than there is in trying to visualize the nature of a mathematical formula.

But what about those dimensions-time perpendicular to length, breadth and height? Let us return to our car and make our journey around the earth again. We need time for that journey. In a short period we cover a small distance, such a small distance that we try in vain to show the curvature of the earth. In slightly more time the distance covered becomes greater and we can begin to measure the curvature. The farther we drive, the more time passes, and the more curvature we can observe. And the greater the curvature in fact *is* with regard to our point of departure, the point from which we began to count the time. The longer the time, the greater the curvature we may say, and the degree of curvature is dependent on the time which has passed.

Here we have simply replaced the third terrestrial dimension by the dimension of 'time.' In our car we calculated with length, breadth and time. And the time was perpendicular to the length and breadth of the earth's surface—it was after all our third dimension, in which the surface of the earth curved.

The position is much the same in space as well. And space is curved in such a way that a ray of light would return to its starting-point if it did not 'come to grief' on the way, which does in fact happen with most rays.

What is the cause and result of this? Does a ray of light follow a curved path because space is curved, or is space curved because a ray of light follows a curved path?

Einstein provided the answer. He discovered that what we call matter and what is to us energy are essentially the same. They can even be transformed into one another. It was the atom bomb which proved to everyone the clear and terrible truth of this theory. There is therefore no essential difference between matter and energy. Matter has mass, weight—energy has these as well. This explains the increase in mass of a space ship which approaches the speed of light, its energy of movement has weight as well!

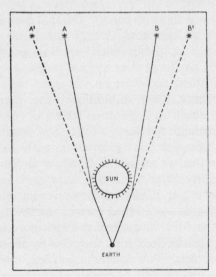

Einstein contended—the astronomer confirmed it! This drawing shows in pictorial form the principle of the way in which astronomers provided the proof of the correctness of Einstein's assertion that a ray of light does not follow a straight path, but is curved in the neighbourhood of matter. They measured the distance apart of two stars, to our eyes, at a time when the sun was not 'in the neighbourhood.' They measured the distance once again when the sun was in such a position that the rays of light from the two stars had to pass along the sun on their way to the earth. Since that is not normally possible—when the sun is shining we do not see the stars—they had to wait for a total solar eclipse. During that eclipse the astronomers measured the distance between the two stars, as seen by our eyes, and these stars appeared to be farther apart than when the sun was not there! A look at the drawing will make the point clear immediately. When the sun was not there, the astronomers saw the two stars at the points A and B. When the sun was there, the rays of light from the stars initially followed a straight line, but in the region of the sun they were bent somewhat towards that heavenly body, so that their direction changed. However, the astronomers naturally saw the stars in the direction from which the rays reached them, that is at points A^I and B^I. The difference could clearly be measured. It was by no means as large as suggested in the drawing, amounting to not more than a few hundredths of a millimetre on the photographic plate. In the drawing all the proportions are incorrect, but that is to make the position clearer.

Light is also a form of energy. Light has weight. Oh, light is very light, at least according to terrestrial standards. On the basis of a very low price per kilowatt we would have to pay a few hundred thousand pounds for a kilogramme of electric light. It may however be mentioned that the sun sends us a few hundreds of tons of light quite free every twenty-four hours!

The fact that light has mass is the reason why rays of light do not follow a 'straight' line in space. For, like all mass, light is subject to the force of attraction of matter in the universe. Just as the earth is attracted by the sun, light rays are influenced by matter. In the region of suns and other collections of matter in the universe, light rays are deflected, more in the region of large masses, and less in the region of smaller masses. Our sun just possesses a sufficient mass to cause a deflection which we can measure in the rays of light which travel on their path from a star to the earth through the sphere of influence, the 'field of gravity' of the sun. Einstein calculated the degree of that deflection in a concrete case and astronomers put the result to the test, not once, but several times. The calculated figure agreed with that found by experiment.

Every particle of matter deflects light—the total amount of matter present in the universe is just sufficient to make the deflection large enough so that a ray of light which does not come to grief 'returns to itself.' The reason for the curvature of space is therefore the presence of matter. Inconceivable? Just think of Switzerland, where the surface of the earth is highly curved as a result of the presence of enormous quantities of matter which we call mountains!

The universe is consequently curved because it contains matter. And this curvature is also responsible for the phenomenon which we call 'the force of gravity.' The force of gravity does not exist at all—at least, not as a 'force.' It is a consequence of the curvature of space. Our sun, an enormous sphere of matter, curves the space around it so strongly that the earth follows that curvature and thereby describes an orbit around the sun. There is consequently no question of the sun exerting a 'force' on the earth.

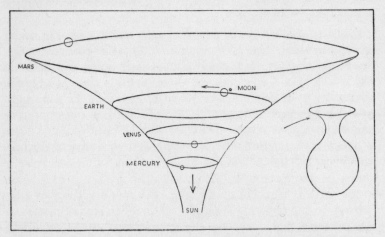

The curvature of space can be illustrated roughly by these drawings. On the right we see a vase with a narrow neck which widens out. If we throw a marble into the vase from the side, then it will, before falling through the narrow neck, circle round a few times above the opening, against the sloping wall of the neck. The force of gravity and friction are the reasons why it does this a few times only. If these forces could however be eliminated, then the marble would continue to circle round without falling into the vase. The curved form of the neck is the reason why the marble continues to describe a circular path. And not merely this, since the nearer the opening, the faster the marble will circle round. If we now look at the larger drawing, we see a similar situation. We must however think of the slope of the 'neck' as being flatter and wider towards the top. The sun causes the curvature of space, the neck, and as a result of the curvature the planets or marbles circle round in the neck, forced into their path by the form of the neck. A real 'force' is consequently not exerted at all. And, the nearer the opening, the faster the planet moves! Mercury moves like one possessed in order not to 'fall'. Above Mars we must imagine the other planets. Pluto, for example, revolves where the 'neck' is already virtually flat. This is why it need only move so slowly!

Let us see what consequences this all has. Curved space returns to itself, just as the earth's surface does. It is therefore unlimited, just as the earth's surface is. We can travel on the earth as far as we want to, we shall never find a limit beyond which the surface ceases, and the same is true of space. Yet space is not infinite. The earth is not either, its unlimited surface has a magnitude which can if desired be worked out exactly in square centimetres. Naturally science has not so far been able to calculate space as accurately as the earth's surface. It can do no more than make estimates. By doing that, it states cautiously that the radius of the universe, that is half the diameter, is at this moment something like 10 milliard light years. It has also made a supposition concerning the amount of matter in the universe. That amount is estimated by some scholars as three times ten to the seventy-fourth atoms, which is, expressed briefly $3 \cdot 10^{74}$, and written out in full:

300,000,000,000,000,000,000,000,000,000,000,000,000,
000,000,000,000,000,000,000,000,000,000,000,000.

This number can no longer be expressed in billions, trillions or any other units. Its magnitude is also inconceivable.[1]

Let us just try to obtain an impression. The population of the world is estimated at 2 milliard souls. Let us assume that there are in the universe 2 milliard worlds which are populated just as densely as our own. In all there are then 4 trillion souls. We train all these 4 trillion people to be typists who do not, as do real artists at the typewriter, strike 500 keys per minute, but can strike no fewer than a million keys a minute. We set them all at work and let them type at full speed, day and night, without eating, drinking or sleeping, making a million strokes

[1] See also Chapter XV.

per minute per person without any interruption. After how long will they together have made a total of $3 \cdot 10^{74}$ strokes? A day, a month, a year, a century? Every day they achieve in all the respectable total of 5,000 quadrillion strokes. Yet they would have to work on for no less than 150 times a trillion times a quadrillion years in order to reach the required number. I doubt whether anyone can imagine just how long this is!

There is therefore quite a lot of matter in the universe, and yet—it is virtually empty. Without exaggeration it can be said that if the universe could exist completely without matter, it would not differ in any way from what it is at present. The American astronomer Hubble once estimated the average density of the matter in the universe. On the earth it amounts to a few trillion atoms per cubic centimetre. Hubble assumed that the matter in space is not concentrated in suns, planets and the like, but is spread quite uniformly throughout space. In that case, he concluded, there would not be more than a few atoms in every cubic metre of space. In the most perfect vacuum which we can make on earth there are however still untold billions of atoms in each cubic metre. The English astronomer, Jeans, found a striking comparison for this. A swarm of wasps which would be relatively just as 'dense' as the matter in the universe would not find things very congenial, since a total of three wasps would be swarming about above the whole of Europe.

Space is inconceivably large. Our sight can penetrate only into $1 \cdot 5\%$ of it—now a remark in an earlier chapter becomes clear. Almost everywhere there is nothing. Here and there a bit of matter, a sun, a number of suns together, a galaxy. And all those systems are escaping from one another, let us remember. Where are they escaping to? Not towards the limits of the universe, for the universe has no limits.

Reasoning in this way, we do not reach a satisfactory answer. The position is, after all, different. The galaxies are not escaping from one another at all in the literal sense of the word.

We had a reason for saying that the radius of the universe was *at this moment* something like 10 milliard light years. That radius is in fact not a fixed magnitude—it is becoming larger and larger. In other words, the universe is expanding. Space is becoming larger and larger and the galaxies and groups of galaxies are being dragged along in that expansion. It is the same as with a child's balloon. If we stick little bits of paper right next to one another on the rubber and then blow the balloon up, the bits of paper will be farther and farther apart. During blowing up they all move farther from one another without exception. The surface of the balloon becomes larger; the bits of paper are not escaping from one another at all— they are merely being taken along by the expansion of the surface of the balloon. This is also the fate of the galaxies, of our galaxy, as well as of the milliards of others. We are involved in the expansion of the universe as well.

Where is space expanding to? Obviously to something which is not space. But what is that 'something'?

Here 'logical' reasoning threatens to run aground again. We must not phrase the question in this way. We must cast aside our earthly concepts and our limited logic completely. We must satisfy ourselves here with a purely mathematical approach. We can only conclude that the universe is expanding in the fourth dimension, in time. In common English: we can say no more than that the universe is becoming larger as more time passes, just as the surface of a balloon gets larger as we blow longer.

Mathematicians can say all this precisely, in formulae. They too give up any idea of clarity, and from their formulae it can only be deduced that space and time are in their deepest nature one, just as matter and energy are in essence one. Space and time cannot be separated from one another, they determine one another. The men of science say that we live in a 'four-dimensional space-time continuum.'

Those who do not believe it must just look through a large telescope. They will see the space-time continuum before their eyes. For whoever looks into space at the same time sees back into time. He will, for example, see in the telescope two spiral nebulae 'next to' one another, one 10 million the other 20 million light years away from us. He is not seeing those nebulae in their present form, their present state, their present relationships. He sees one as it was 10 million years ago and the other in its situation of 20 million years ago. After all, the light has taken respectively 10 million and 20 million years to reach the observer and it gives merely a picture of its origin as it was at the moment it was emitted. If a galaxy a million light years away 'now' ceases to exist, we could nevertheless still see it existing for a further million years.

No one can therefore say what it is like at any particular point in the universe 'at the moment.' We do not even see the moon as it is—we see it as it was a second ago, for moonlight takes one second to reach the earth.

Whoever receives pictures from the universe in a telescope is seeing back into time. And not only that. He is also seeing a condition 10 million and one of 20 million years ago at one and the same moment. He does not see the 'present'—but each moment of the past, as far as the telescope reaches. This results from the great distances, from space. Time and space are for his eye connected to one another, they are one. For each point in his field of view there is a time which belongs to that point, which is one with it and which differs from any other time, just as each point differs from another in its distance from us.

Astronomers can likewise say nothing about the universe in its present state, nor about its position a million years ago. The telescope certainly provides a picture of what it was like a million years ago at a certain distance from us, but the telescope does not tell us anything about what it was like a million years ago at other distances. An 'instant exposure' of the whole of the universe could not therefore be given, even if we had telescopes which could explore the whole of space. And this is, as we have said, definitely not the case.

This time factor makes the investigation of the universe extremely difficult, of course. We may well be surprised at how much astronomy and science have nevertheless succeeded in learning. How long has scientific research been going on? A few hundred years. Now that we have come to the end of our journey through the macrocosm we know what a few hundred years are on the clock of the universe, where millions of years glide past as if they were seconds.

CHAPTER X

THE ALCHEMISTS AND THEIR ELEMENTS. THE DISCOVERY OF
THE PHILOSOPHER'S STONE. ATOMS—A TYPE OF MINIATURE
SOLAR SYSTEM. RADIOACTIVITY CAN BE DANGEROUS

Gold! That is what the medieval alchemists wanted to make.
Shrouded in the greatest possible mystery, they worked away
in their obscure dens with metals, ores and liquids, in retorts
and tubes, using fires and bellows. Gold—the noblest of the
metals! Whoever succeeded in making that from other, base
metals would be rich, unimaginably rich, the richest man in the
world. The alchemists toiled away in their smoky laboratories.
The rulers of the world, for ever embarrassed for more money,
followed the experiments of their protégés with something
between an excited interest and an interested excitement. An
alchemist would often announce that he had found the philosopher's stone, the means for making gold artificially, for transform-
ing one element into the other. Just as often, however, he appeared
to have been mistaken, or to have been a common impostor.

The centuries passed. The philosopher's stone was not
discovered. Generations came and generations went, and from
the mixing, boiling and filtering of the alchemists there slowly
emerged scientific chemistry which, once it had fully developed,
finally spoke the redeeming word: 'the philosopher's stone does
not exist and cannot exist.'

And once that had been irrefutably established, the philosopher's stone was in fact discovered in the nineteenth year of
the twentieth century. The finder was not an alchemist
mumbling incantations, but a sober, modern scientist. The
discovery did not take place in a smoky den full of strange
equipment, in mysterious vessels and with the help of huge
fires, but in a business-like, cool science laboratory. Gold did
not appear from a base metal—oxygen and hydrogen were
formed from nitrogen and helium.

Lord Rutherford was the first man to succeed in making one element from another and was the finder of the philosopher's stone, a 'stone' which turned out to be quite different from what all the medieval alchemists had imagined even in their most audacious dreams. It was however the means by which artificial gold could be made if desired.

The manufacture of artificial gold has however never been undertaken on a large scale. It would not have served any purpose, since it would be much more expensive than natural gold, and moreover, there were infinitely more valuable things than gold to be made using the philosopher's stone or, as it is now called, 'nuclear transmutation,' things which are called 'radioactive isotopes' and which are of inestimable value in medicine, industry, agriculture and in many other fields.

In their search for gold the alchemists did sterling service in the development of chemistry. They did, in fact, make gold in the figurative sense, but gold in the literal sense continued to elude them, since they started from quite incorrect premises.

In common with the Greek philosophers, the ancient alchemists considered that all matter was constructed from four different materials or elements, and that all possible substances known to them consisted of combinations of these elements in different proportions. Earth, air, fire and water, those were the basic materials or elements. It is not for nothing that we continue to speak of 'the elements' when we talk about a storm at sea in which 'the elements are let loose.'

According to the alchemists, metals, for example, consisted of the elements earth and fire. In the base metals there was a lot of earth and a little fire, in the noble ones, a little earth and a lot of fire. It must consequently have been possible in a metal such as copper to alter the proportion between the earth and fire, so that gold would be formed.

The alchemists' opinions have, of course, long been relinquished, but the concept 'element' has been preserved, although it today means something quite different from earth, air, fire and water. An element is a substance which remains itself under all circumstances and which cannot be broken down or changed by any chemical trick. Ninety-two of these substances occur in nature and, in recent years, a further ten have been made in

94

laboratories. This is consequently a long way from the four which the alchemists insisted upon.

Is water an element? It can be attacked by electricity whereby it is decomposed into two gases, namely oxygen and hydrogen, which can again be transformed into water. Water is consequently not an element. Air? A mixture of oxygen, nitrogen and small amounts of other gases. Common salt is likewise no more an element than air, since it can be decomposed into the metal sodium and the gas chlorine.

There are thousands of materials which can be broken down in all sorts of ways, so that they lose their original properties and give rise to other substances with quite different properties. This cannot, however, be done with 92 substances. Hydrogen remains hydrogen, copper remains copper, barium remains barium, whatever chemical tricks are performed on them. For the sake of convenience, we will not consider the ten artificial elements in this book, although everything that is true of the others applies to them as well.[1]

Everything in nature—whether it be dead or alive—is made up from these 92 elements, for example, the earth, the planets, houses, telephones, the sun, the stars, books—everything.

A piece of carbon cannot, therefore, be split chemically into other materials. It can nevertheless be attacked with a knife. Small pieces can be cut from it, and these can be cut again, and so on. The question now arises as to whether this process can be carried out indefinitely. Is there not an amount of carbon which is so small that it cannot be sub-divided?

This question was studied by scientists for a long time, and an answer was found. Such an amount does, in fact, exist. These scientists reverted to the concept of matter formulated centuries before by the Greek philosopher Democritus, namely that everything in the world consists in the final analysis of small, indivisible particles. The Greek word for indivisible is 'atomos,' and the small, indivisible particles were therefore called 'atoms.' The element carbon can be very finely sub-divided, but we cannot obtain smaller particles than carbon atoms from it.

The thousands of substances known to us are nothing but compounds or mixtures in all sorts of proportions and forms of atoms of the ninety-two elements. The smallest unit of common

[1] There is a complete list of the elements in the Appendix.

95

salt is consequently not an atom, since it consists of atoms of sodium and chlorine. The smallest unit of a substance which is not an element is called a molecule. Atoms of the same type also nearly always form molecules, probably according to the saying 'the more we are together . . .'!

The whole world is built up from 92 different substances. Nature is consequently unsurveyable, but science does not like such a position, so that a rapid attempt was made to create some order out of this chaos. Could not the 92 elements be classified nicely in some way or another? The German, Lothar Meyer, and the Russian, Dimitri Mendeleev, hit upon the same idea—as has happened more than once—at approximately the same time. What would happen if the elements were arranged in a series in the order of their weight, beginning with the lightest and finishing with the heaviest? It became a trim series, hydrogen first, then helium, followed by lithium, and so on, up to the heaviest element, uranium, which consequently occupied the ninety-second place.

When the work was completed, Meyer and Mendeleev could well be pleased, for the result was astonishing. By arranging the elements according to their weights, they had, at a single stroke, packed all nature nicely into a box. There appeared, in fact, to be a system in the elements. In their work Meyer and Mendeleev had not made use of any of the chemical properties, state or character of the substances—it was solely a question of their weight; yet in their series the elements also appeared to be arranged strictly according to their nature! In the sequence of the elements all sorts of properties alternated with one another and always in the same order. The materials from which nature was constructed did not, therefore, form an arbitrary and unrelated collection. A certain basic relationship and agreement must exist between the atoms of different substances.

It was obvious that the next question was to discover what an atom really was. A piece of copper and a tube of hydrogen gas are outwardly totally different, but was their nature then so very different?

No, said the English scholar, Lord Rutherford, after exhaustive investigations. He dispensed once and for all with the idea that an atom was an extremely small piece of material, both indivisible and immutable.

He made the discovery that the world is really a great illusion, since atoms appeared to consist to the extent of more than 99% of nothing. In 1911 he discovered that an atom consists of various particles which, when packed together, are much smaller than the space they occupy as an atom. The real matter is in the nucleus of the atom and this carries a positive charge. Outside that nucleus particles with a negative charge describe elliptical, almost circular paths at high speeds around the nucleus. These negatively charged particles, called electrons, have collectively just as high a negative charge as there is a positive charge in the nucleus, so that, under normal circumstances, the atom is outwardly neutral. The distances between the electrons and the nucleus are very much larger than the diameter of the particles.

Does not this description remind you of something? Yes . . . the solar system! A sun, with planets revolving around it and at various distances from it; a system consisting mainly of nothing, of space between masses of material which, when packed together, would be much smaller than the space which the system now occupies.

Yes, the atom is nothing more nor less than a sort of miniature solar system. It was initially thought that it was even a 'reduced edition' of our great system, but there soon appeared to be essential differences between the macrocosm and the world of the atom. Be this as it may, the parallel is striking, particularly as regards the space in the atom and the solar system. If one could pack together all the 'real' matter of the atoms of which a man consists, without any space between them, how much space would a man then occupy? It sounds strange, but it is really true, if we could do this, we should have about enough matter to fill the eye of a darning-needle. Such a darning-needle would, however, then weigh just as much as a man, so that darning with it would involve certain difficulties.

From the material point of view, man is, consequently, really nothing. He contains something like one cubic millimetre of 'real' matter, the rest is empty space. This applies to everything in the universe, with the exception of a certain category of stars, the matter of which, in fact, appears to be packed together in the same way as in our darning-needle, and which must, therefore, weigh thousands of kilogrammes per square centimetre according to terrestrial standards. Is nature, therefore, a great illusion, or not?

Precisely how large, or rather, how small is an atom? The Dutch physicist, Dr. H. Groot, has given an idea of this by means of a very charming comparison. Take, he says, a bacteria having a length of a thousandth of a millimetre, and place an atom beside it. Then magnify both to the same extent. When the magnification is a million times, the bacteria will be 1 metre long, and the atom will have a diameter of 0·1 millimetre. Magnify this once again a million times. The bacteria is then 1,000 kilometres long, while the atom will have a diameter of 100 metres. And in that atom 100 metres in length we will find, after a long search, the nucleus with all the matter, having a diameter of 1 *millimetre*.

All atoms are consequently types of solar systems. The question now arises as to what extent oxygen atoms differ from silver atoms. How do atoms differ from one another? The differences lie in the composition of the nucleus, and in the number of electrons round that nucleus.

The lightest and simplest nucleus is that of the hydrogen atom. It consists of one single positively charged particle, a proton. A single electron describes its path round this nucleus. An electron is 1,840 times as light as a proton—this being why it contributes hardly anything to the weight of the atom. The nucleus of the helium atom, the gas which comes after hydrogen in the system of Meyer and Mendeleev—the 'periodic system of the elements'—is somewhat more complicated. Two electrons revolve round its nucleus. Since the atom is, as a whole, electrically neutral, there must be two positive charges in the nucleus. The nucleus must, therefore, consist of two protons. But a child knows that like electrical charges repel one another. How then can that helium nucleus exist? Nature has however provided guardians of the peace. The helium nucleus consists of four particles, not of two. There are, in fact, two protons in it, that is two hydrogen nuclei. The nuclei of all atoms consist of hydrogen plus guardians of the peace. We could, therefore, state that all creation is nothing but hydrogen. Be this as it may, the helium nucleus contains two protons. It also contains two neutrons. These are particles which are virtually the same as protons, but have no electrical charge. They are neutral—hence their name. In the nucleus these neutrons fulfil the function of policemen, who preserve the peace between people who cannot stand one another. How they precisely do this is still a secret. Physicists speak about certain 'nuclear forces,' about which they know much, the nature of which however still eludes them.

There is a strict logic in the construction of atoms. The third element of the periodic system, lithium, has three electrons, the fourth, beryllium, four, etc., up to number 92, uranium, in which a cloud of 92 electrons whirls round the nucleus. The number of protons in the nucleus, of course, increases by one in each case as the number of electrons on the outside increases. Uranium therefore has 92 protons in its nucleus, but the number of policemen is not 92. Two policemen are sufficient to preserve the peace between two fighters, but to keep 92 protons under control it seems that nature needs more than 92 neutrons. No fewer than 146 seem necessary, and yet the peace in the uranium nucleus is only very relative. Its nucleus, therefore, consists of 92 protons and 146 neutrons, and is 238 times as heavy as the hydrogen nucleus. In other words, uranium has an atomic weight of 238.

At least. . . . There is also uranium with an atomic weight of 235. Its nucleus does not contain 146, but 143 neutrons. These two forms of uranium do not differ chemically, they are both precisely the same material. Almost all atoms show this behaviour. Hydrogen, for example, also has a heavier brother, a sort of hydrogen with not only one proton in its nucleus, but also one neutron. This form has gradually become famous as heavy hydrogen or deuterium. There is even a very heavy brother, tritium, which has one proton and two neutrons in its nucleus. Almost all elements are composed of atoms which are chemically identical, but whose weight can differ by one or more neutrons. Atoms of the same element, having a different atomic weight, are called *isotopes*, which means 'occupying the same place.' After all, they occupy the same place in the periodic system! In their normal state all elements consist of a mixture of isotopes. It is only in the laboratory that they can be separated. Uranium-238 (abbreviated as U^{238}) and uranium-235 (U^{235}) are, consequently, isotopes, as are hydrogen and deuterium.

Whereas the number of neutrons in the nucleus of a given element can change somewhat, the number of protons is always

99

the same, for this number determines the nature of the material. An element with eight protons in its nucleus is oxygen. A nucleus with one proton less is not oxygen, but nitrogen.

Rutherford's discovery made it possible to obtain an insight into what goes on inside the world of the atom. We have succeeded in explaining how it is that all types of elements can combine with one another and form new substances. All chemical reactions are interactions between the electrons in atoms. When sodium and chlorine form common salt, nothing happens except that chlorine takes over one electron from sodium. Chlorine thereby acquires a negative charge and sodium a positive one, so that they attract one another and together form a molecule of common salt. In all chemical reactions, however complicated they may be, only the electrons play a part—the nuclei of the atoms remain the same and nothing happens to them. An element can consequently never be altered chemically. If only the ancient alchemists had known that.

The atom was not then the solid, indivisible particle it had been thought to be. The nucleus was however apparently like that, or . . . perhaps not? Rutherford did not think so. He started experimenting, and was found to be right. He found the philosopher's stone. Rutherford did not concern himself with the electrons, but directed his attention to the nucleus of the atom. He took the element nitrogen, whose nucleus consists of seven protons and seven neutrons. He succeeded in bombarding the nitrogen nucleus with a helium nucleus, consisting of two protons and two neutrons, and in this way obtained a nucleus with nine protons and nine neutrons. This nucleus did not however accept this, and expelled one proton, namely a hydrogen nucleus. There remained a nucleus with eight protons and nine neutrons, i.e. a nucleus of the element oxygen! What had happened? Rutherford had transformed one element into another! The old alchemists had been right, after all. You could make one element from another—providing you knew how to go about it.

Fine, but how could Rutherford start bombarding with helium? He was able to do this thanks to radium, the element discovered by Madame Curie.

This Polish lady, who had become French by her marriage,

was very interested in the mysterious rays which uranium crystals appeared to emit and which had been discovered by the Frenchman Becquerel on the photographic plate with its cross. She began to study uranium systematically and came across a substance which emitted much more powerful radiations than uranium. She succeeded in isolating this substance in the chemically pure state and called it radium, which means 'that which radiates.' Radium appeared to be an, as yet, undiscovered element, which also fitted in well in the filing-cabinet of Meyer and Mendeleev, in place 88, having an atomic weight of 226.

Radium certainly caused some trouble! Instead of being grateful for the shelter it had obtained and remaining quietly in its place, it behaved quite improperly. It turned the whole periodic system, which fitted together so well, upside down, by not observing the law which held there, namely that each element always remains itself. For the element radium did not remain radium. It emitted three types of radiation and changed a few times into another element until, tired of romping, it came to rest as the element lead. This was so revolutionary that scientists immediately began to study radium rays, assuming that they could provide the solution of the mystery.

And they were able to. Radium appeared, in the first place, to emit particles consisting of two protons and two neutrons, in other words, helium nuclei. One element thus resulted automatically from the other! The second type of radiation appeared to consist of electrons. They were not electrons which had revolved round the radium nuclei, but came from the nucleus. And there were no electrons present there at all? The only possible explanation was that a neutron in the nucleus had changed into a proton and had, consequently, released a negative charge which was expelled with great force. The third type of radiation appeared to be an electromagnetic vibration, similar to light, but having a much shorter wavelength. This arose because the changing nucleus had an excess of energy, which it had to get rid of.

Rutherford's bombardment consequently amounted to irradiating nitrogen with the help of radium.

But what a state of affairs had arisen in the meantime! Not only radium, but also uranium and a number of other elements played tricks with the periodic system, by changing, some rapidly, others extremely slowly, into other elements. What was it that drove these elements to such activity, such 'radioactivity'?

The police did not seem to be equal to their task, that was it. The neutrons in the nuclei of the heavy elements, such as radium and uranium, were not, in the long run, in a position to keep the repelling protons sufficiently under control. A constant uproar seemed to prevail in the nuclei. The link between the nuclear particles was only so so, and the result was that fragments of the nucleus broke away, choosing freedom at great speeds. In some types of atoms the process of 'radioactive disintegration' appeared to take place very rapidly, in others very slowly. Each type even seemed to preserve its own tempo, which could not be changed by anything or by anyone. This radiation goes on all the time, under all circumstances, and stops only when all the atoms of the material have disintegrated into others.

What nature had been doing since the beginning of time, Rutherford copied in 1919, and he was followed by other modern 'alchemists,' for the method of bombardment appeared to produce very surprising results. The new elements formed after bombardment did not appear to be merely phosphorus or merely nitrogen—they were *radioactive* phosphorus and *radioactive* nitrogen! And they emitted rays just like the other radioactive elements, until they had in turn disintegrated into stable elements. They were consequently radioactive isotopes and appeared to be of great potential value, not only to science itself, but also to medicine, for example, as well as agriculture and industry, to mention only a few fields.

There are however two sides to every question, and this is also true of the radioactive elements. They have great advantages, but also great disadvantages. They are, in fact, dangerous. The helium nuclei, the electrons, the gamma rays (as the electromagnetic vibration, the third type of radium rays, are called), the neutron radiation—for that exists as well—can damage living organisms. Since these organisms consist, as we have seen, for the most part of space, many rays penetrate into them and in their rapid passage they rip off particles of the atoms of which the living cells consist. This can give rise to malformations, tumours, the decay of cells, and to death.

Nobody yet knows how great the danger is. Radioactive

radiation is at the moment the subject of great anxiety, but also of very intensive study. Nobody knows its long-term consequences. Perhaps—and let us hope so—they will be much less serious than people think at the moment. That will be discovered in due course, but as long as we are groping in the dark we are taking the most extensive precautionary and protective measures, which is quite understandable.

CHAPTER XI

'A further 30 centimetres.'

Slowly the man draws the rod 30 centimetres out. An indicator rises hesitatingly over a dial and then falls back to its previous position. There is a gentle click which becomes faster and then slower.

'A further 30 centimetres.'

The man pulls. The pointer rises and falls, followed by a ticking, faster, then slower.

'The last rod. 30 centimetres.'

The last rod is pulled out. The pointer rises and then stays in position. The faster ticking continues. Many eyes are watching the dial. The pointer stays in position.

The age of nuclear energy has begun. The date was 2nd December, 1942, at half-past three in the afternoon, in Chicago. The man who will live on in history as the practical initiator of that age was the Italian scientist, Enrico Fermi.

In a town elsewhere in America, a smile must have been on the lips of the man who, about thirty years before, had laid the theoretical basis for Fermi's practical work. On hearing the news from Chicago, Albert Einstein must have smiled. Nature had once again confirmed the correctness of his theories.

The age of nuclear energy had opened, and radioactivity had been the key to it.

It was all very logical. There occur in nature elements which emit radiations and which in doing so are transformed. Man learnt this art from nature and changed various elements into others. The French couple Joliot-Curie, for example, bombarded aluminium with helium nuclei which had been radiated by a radioactive element. As a result, radioactive phosphorus was formed from aluminium, and on emitting a radiation this became silicon. Experiments with radiation were carried out everywhere and, it could hardly have been otherwise, a fourth sort of ray was discovered. Chadwick was the man who identified this type as a radiation of neutrons. The neutral particles of the atomic nuclei also appeared to be able to live an independent life!

This really set things going, for neutrons turned out to be ideal projectiles for scientific bombardments. Up till then people had had to make do with helium nuclei, which are called alpha particles. Make do was the operative word, since alpha particles have, after all, a positive charge, and the nuclei at which they were fired were positive as well. If an alpha particle is to penetrate into a nucleus, then it has to overcome the strong electrical repulsion. The neutron is however neutral, does not therefore attract electrical charges, and wanders in anywhere. It turns the nucleus upside down, a neutron changes into a proton and an electron, and the next heaviest element is formed!

The next step was obvious. What would happen if neutrons were fired at nuclei of uranium, which is the heaviest of all known elements? Would a heavier element then be formed than the heaviest which occurs in nature? In other words, would scientists then have made a new element, have created a substance which had not previously existed?

The Germans, Otto Hahn, Lise Meitner and Fritz Strassman wanted to be sure. In 1938 they began a number of very careful experiments in Berlin. They directed a stream of neutrons at a uranium preparation. Would a so-called trans-uranium be formed? They were surprised by the result. The substance they found after radiation looked very much like barium, a well-known element in the middle of the periodic system. If it had been a close neighbour of uranium, then there would certainly have been an explanation. But this . . . Otto Hahn shook his head.

Lise Meitner was the first who dared to utter the bold supposition. It needed courage, for what she said was in conflict with everything scientists considered possible. The neutron, she said, has not caused a new element to be formed. It has penetrated with such force into the uranium nucleus that that nucleus has broken up into pieces which are nuclei of lighter elements!

She was right. For the assumed barium was barium, and apart from barium krypton had also been formed, an inert gas from the middle of the periodic system.

Investigations showed that it was uranium-235 which had provided the general surprise and that the resultant substances were barium-144 and krypton-90. Lise Meitner made a calculation and said: Barium has 56 protons in its nucleus and krypton 36, that is in all 92, the number of uranium. The uranium nucleus had broken into two pieces and the pieces had flown apart at a high speed.

How did they attain that high speed? How do all radioactive elements acquire the energy necessary to emit particles or a vibration? There is nothing or no one, there is no single external source which provides the energy. That energy must come from the nucleus itself without it first being placed there.

Something comes out of the nucleus which was not in it as such. Strange, but stranger still, something is lost which was there before.

Calculations, weighings and measurements were carried out. Something was not right with the weight. If a uranium nucleus were weighed, then a nucleus of barium and one of krypton, and if account were taken of everything that had happened during the bombardment, then matter had been lost! The uranium nucleus was heavier than everything which had been formed from it. Where was that weight, that matter? Energy which was not there appeared, and matter which was there disappeared.

Einstein had foretold that decades ago! He had said that matter and energy are the same in essence and can be transformed into one another. There is even a fixed relationship to cover it. The energy into which a given amount of matter can be transformed is equal to the mass of that matter multiplied by the square of the speed of light, or expressed as a formula, $E = mc^2$.

That transformation of matter into energy takes place in the atomic nucleus. No one knows how it precisely happens—but it does. A very large amount of energy results from very little matter, for that c^2, or $c \times c$, is very large. The speed of light amounts to 300,000 kilometres per second, but in Einstein's formula it must be given in centimetres per second, so that c^2 becomes 30,000,000,000 × 30,000,000,000. A practical example will make the position clearer. If we could transform 1 *gramme* of matter completely into energy, then we would obtain enough energy to boil 200,000 metric tons of iced water.[1]

In radioactive degradation and the bombardment of U^{235} by no means all the matter is transformed into energy—only that small part which was 'lost.' Yet in this case extremely small parts make an enormous quantity. A kilogramme of U^{235} consists of innumerable quadrillions of atoms and if we split all those atoms we obtain innumerable quadrillions of small 'lost' bits, which are transformed into energy. The total amount of energy produced by the splitting of 1 kilogramme U^{235} is equal to the energy obtained by burning 2,600,000 kilogrammes of coal or 2,500,000 litres of petrol.

Let us then take a kilogramme of U^{235} and place it in an electric power station. People would say: Just turn on! Or: Use it in a car, or in an aeroplane, or in . . .

Yes, if it were only as simple as that, it would be very easy and cheap to convert from coal and petroleum, the world's supplies of which are beginning to fall seriously, to nuclear energy. The problem was, on the contrary, extremely difficult.

The energy is of course released in the form of heat, a very useful form. In order to keep the nuclear fission going, energy had to be supplied, bombardment of uranium had to be carried out. And the amount of energy which had to be supplied was greater than that provided by the fission. For, let us remember, it was here a question of extremely small amounts, with which we work in the laboratory, and the amount of heat formed was negligibly small compared with the amount of energy needed to bring about the nuclear fission. Applied on a large scale, it would be a very uneconomic business. Unless . . .

Unless matters could be so arranged that the nuclear fission, once started, continued of its own accord, much in the same way as a stove, where by the action of one match we can ensure that one piece of coal ignites the other for hours on end, until the fuel is used up.

And that was possible! For Lise Meitner had not yet finished

---

[1] There is a calculation in the Appendix.

her calculations. The proton sum was correct, but what about the neutrons? The nucleus of U^{235} has 143 neutrons, the resultant barium has 88 and krypton 54. Counting the penetrating projectile, the old nucleus had 144 neutrons, the new nuclei had in all 142. There were two neutrons which had not been used by either of the two parties and had therefore been released. Released for ... yes, why not for the purposes of nuclear fission? If these two neutrons could be used as projectiles, they would each be able to split one nucleus, after which there would therefore be four free neutrons, which in their turn ... and so on.

Investigations showed that even more neutrons were released during fission, for the uranium nucleus often also splits into other parts, for example into strontium and xenon. There are quite a number of possibilities for splitting which all agree in that the total number of protons in the newly formed nuclei is always ninety-two. It may be taken as an average that in every fission reaction somewhat more than two neutrons were released and became available as projectiles.

The 'nuclear stove' could consequently burn in theory, but 'fuel' had to be found for it. U^{235} is very scarce. The uranium which occurs in nature consists to the extent of $99 \cdot 3\%$ of another uranium isotope, U^{238}, and this cannot be split. It was therefore a matter of obtaining the $0 \cdot 7\%$ U^{235} from natural uranium. This was both a difficult and expensive business. Nothing can be done chemically, for from this point of view the two isotopes are precisely the same, both being uranium. A solution had to be sought by physical means, based on the difference in weight. After much effort various methods were discovered to separate the isotopes.

Yet the 'nuclear stove' could still not burn in practice, for U^{235} turned out to be able to be split only with neutrons which were not moving too fast—and the projectiles which are released by splitting nuclei have a very high speed. A new problem, a new solution. A substance would have to be found which slows down the neutrons in their passage without absorbing them. For this is also a problem. Many substances like to absorb neutrons. It cannot be said just how much scientists thought, calculated, consulted and sighed, but when the day of 2nd December, 1942, dawned in Chicago, Fermi had theoretically mastered the subject.

Together with his colleagues he had constructed a uranium pile. Rods of uranium and blocks of graphite, a form of carbon, were piled up one on top of the other. Between them were placed rods of cadmium, a substance which absorbs neutrons very eagerly. Fermi did not need a 'match.' Neutrons wander about everywhere and fissions took place in uranium by its very nature. Yet the liberated neutrons were picked up by the cadmium so that they could not cause any new fissions.

But then, on 2nd December, the final test was begun, to the great interest of those present. Slowly Fermi had the cadmium rods drawn out of the uranium pile. At the same time the indicator showed that neutron production had increased, but the cadmium at the same time remained master of the situation, until the last rod was drawn out 30 centimetres farther. Then the neutron production increased again, and remained constant. Good, neutrons were still being absorbed, not only by the small piece of cadmium which was still in the pile, but also by impurities in the graphite and the uranium itself, but just as many neutrons were released in each case as were used up; the fission process kept going by itself, the temperature rose!

Fermi sighed very deeply. It worked. He continued to look, at the first working *nuclear reactor* in the world.

The age of nuclear energy had opened, a development had begun which was in a few years to assume enormous proportions. Less than twenty years after Fermi's deep sigh techniques have advanced so much that there are several kinds of nuclear reactors which all depend on the same principle, but which work in very different ways and with different substances. Most of them are still used only for experimental industrial and scientific research, but both in the United States and Great Britain, as well as in the Soviet Union, nuclear reactors are already working for the common good, for the generation of electricity. Power stations have been built in these countries where there are no piles of coal and boiler-houses, where the steam for the turbines is no longer made by bringing water to the boil using coal. Nuclear reactors have been built in these power stations, and the heat which is liberated during the fission process is used to heat water to give steam. The Americans have built submarines which are propelled by nuclear reactors. The Russians have used an ice-breaker which derives power from nuclear reactors to break and keep open channels in the far north.

Work has been going on very rapidly since World War II to master the many difficult problems which have arisen, such as the obtaining of U^{235}, the finding of suitable substances for slowing down neutrons, the designing of regulating and measuring devices, the manufacture of materials for screening reactors.

This last point was particularly important, for not only is uranium itself radioactive, but the products of fission are all the more so. Some of these radioactive isotopes are transformed only very slowly into stable elements. The heart of the reactor must consequently be well screened, because of the danger of radioactive radiation. Care must also be taken that no radioactive material can escape in any way from the reactor. Lead turned out to be an excellent screening material. Its only disadvantage is that it is very heavy and makes the reactors unwieldy and unmanageable. During recent years satisfactory results have also been obtained with certain types of concrete. This point has by no means yet been fully studied, although screening is already in normal cases thoroughly adequate.

We said that Fermi's successful experiment had opened up the age of nuclear energy. This is not the whole story. Fermi opened up the *peaceful* atomic age—for there is unfortunately another as well, the *military* one. That had already begun a few years earlier with a memorandum from Professor Dr. Albert Einstein to President Roosevelt, in which the scholar warned the statesman that nuclear fission could be used as a weapon and that work was already probably in progress on it in Germany. This memorandum led to a development which was in 1945 the cause of the death of tens of thousands of inhabitants of the Japanese cities of Hiroshima and Nagasaki, and which has determined the post-war course of political events.

After Fermi's nuclear reactor came the atom bomb.

This frightful weapon is the reason why millions of people shudder at the mention of the word nuclear energy and why they have a deep-rooted fear of everything which has to do with atoms, including nuclear reactors.

Fear of a nuclear reactor is, let this be stressed, quite unfounded. Accidents can of course happen with a reactor, just as with any technical installation. The consequences of those accidents can be serious, just as those of an explosion in a gas-works, a laundry, or anywhere else. But that is not what people are afraid of. Their fear relates to the danger of a nuclear explosion, that is the danger that a reactor might explode like an atom bomb. And this is now absolutely impossible!

An atom bomb and a nuclear reactor both work with nuclear energy—and that is the *only* similarity. A car engine and a cigarette lighter both work with petrol. A reactor would however no more explode like a bomb than a car would run on a cigarette lighter.

In a nuclear energy bomb the fission of all the atomic nuclei present is brought about in a fraction of a second. Pure fissile material, brought together in a large amount, is subject to spontaneous fission. There is always a neutron in the neighbour-hood which causes fission in an amount of fissile material. If the amount of material is so large that the two neutrons which are formed cannot escape to the outside, but have of necessity to touch other nuclei, then two nuclei split, four neutrons are liberated, which split four nuclei, release eight neutrons, and so on. There is an avalanche which spreads in the fraction of a second until all the atoms present and all the energy of fission is released in that same fraction of a second. The formula $E = mc^2$ indicates the amount of force involved.

This avalanche only begins when the amount of fissile material has exceeded a certain limit. What that limit is, is of course kept a strict secret by military authorities. This deter-mining amount of fissile material has been called the 'critical mass.'

In the bomb there is consequently no question of substances absorbing neutrons, regulating apparatus and the like, any more than there is any question of an explosive critical mass in a reactor. Yet the fissile material is always placed in the reactor *divided up* and can therefore never reach an explosive critical mass. And this is just what does happen in the bomb. Various amounts of fissile material are placed in it, each being a long way below the critical mass, and being kept away from one another. There is still no danger of an explosion, but at the moment when the explosion has to take place, the separate amounts are united by means of a certain mechanism to form one, this new amount

III

lying above the critical mass. And at the same moment the bomb explodes.

We have used the word 'fissile material' no fewer than six times in a few paragraphs. There is a reason for this, for an alternate use of 'fissile material' and 'uranium' would have been nicer from a stylistic point of view, but incorrect! The atom bomb does not work with uranium, as is in most cases assumed. Uranium is certainly the basic material for the weapon, but the explosion occurs in plutonium, the ninety-fourth element, the second artificial one. Plutonium is made from uranium, just as Joliot-Curie made phosphorus from aluminium.

And uranium splits into lighter nuclei? Yes, but, as we have said, only the isotope U^{235}, which constitutes $0\cdot7\%$ of natural uranium. The remaining $99\cdot3\%$ of U^{238} does not split under the force of a neutron bombardment.

The reason for this differing behaviour is obvious if we consider the role which the neutrons play in the atomic nucleus, namely that of policemen. In the nucleus of U^{238} there are 146 neutrons to keep 92 repelling protons in order. This succeeds only partly in the long run—hence the radioactivity of these atoms. The 146 men are however sufficient to stop a sudden impact. If a neutron penetrates inside the nucleus, then the mysterious nuclear forces have the opportunity of keeping matters in order, even if it is with difficulty. The position is different with U^{235}. There are 143 neutrons in place of 146 in the nucleus, and those three neutrons less are the reason why on the penetration of a neutron the position can no longer be saved. In the case of a sudden attack the policemen are powerless.

The isotopes U^{238} and U^{235} are mixed in natural uranium. For most types of nuclear reactors the content of $0\cdot7\%$ U^{235} is insufficient, and we are therefore forced to separate U^{235} in the pure state at great expense, and to add it to the natural uranium. We then speak of enriched uranium. There is therefore also U^{238} in the reactor, unsplittable, but subject to the heavy neutron bombardment.

During this bombardment the nucleus of U^{238} accepts a penetrating neutron, just as many other atomic nuclei do, but then the equilibrium in the nucleus is disturbed. A neutron changes into a proton and an electron, the electron is ejected

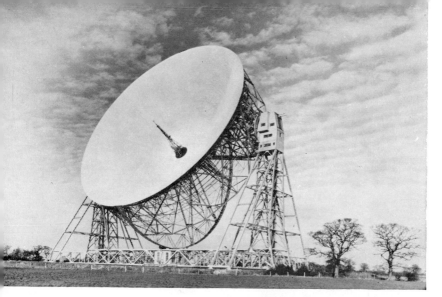

(*Top*) Radio telescopy has opened up new possibilities for astronomers—the collecting and analysis of radio waves from space, instead of light. This is the largest radio telescope in Europe, at Jodrell Bank. It has already proved invaluable in experiments with lunar satellites. (*bottom, from left to right*) The American astronomer E. P. Hubble, who proved that our galaxy is not the whole universe, but merely a very small part of it. Prof. J. H. Oort, the Dutchman, who is director of the observatory in Leyden and president of the International Organization of Astronomers. Prof. Oort is one of the world's outstanding astronomers and has specialized in investigating the nature of our galaxy. Sir Bernard Lovell, director of the radio telescope at Jodrell Bank and professor of radio astronomy at the University of Manchester. He has become famous for his work on experiments with artificial satellites.

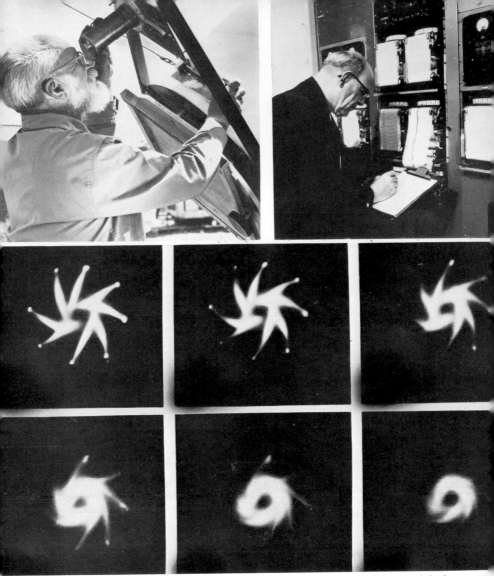

(*Top left*) One of the many American astronomers of Dutch origin is Prof. G. van Biesbroek, who has had a star named after him. The 'Star of Van Biesbroek', which he discovered, is the smallest star known to us. (*top right*) For us the sun is the most important heavenly body. As a result of 'eruptions', it can seriously disturb radio transmissions on earth. This apparatus is used to record the behaviour of the sun, providing material from which experts can draw conclusions and make predictions which can be of great practical use. (*bottom*) How are galaxies formed? A few years ago the American scholar, Dr. W. H. Bostick, succeeded in constructing an apparatus which can imitate the probable course of events. He fired streams of glowing gas at one another under certain physical conditions in a strong magnetic field and photographed the result. This series of photographs shows what happened to the gas in a fraction of a second. In so far as it can be photographed by our telescopes, this is what happens in infinite space in the course of milliards of years.

(*Above left*) This is how a fanciful American artist imagines space travel in the future. Unfortunately there are all too many dreamers in the marginal fields of space travel; nevertheless the drawing is reasonable, and that is something. (*above right*) Dr. Krafft Ehricke, the American expert in space travel, once described mathematically a journey to Venus at a congress on space travel in Copenhagen. He filled boards with formulae, but was still nowhere near Venus! A lot will have to be done before man lands there—if he ever does.

(*Below left*) Dr. Wernher von Braun has already acquired a considerable reputation by his enormous space projects. (*below right*) A cutaway example of the American Vanguard satellite.

(*Left*) E = mc^2. The ghastly practical use of a scientific theory. For the record, this was the twentieth atomic bomb exploded by the Americans. It took place on 30th October, 1951, near Las Vegas. (*bottom left*) The experimental fast fission breeder reactor, Dounreay, Caithness. On the left is the secondary heat exchanger building and, on the right, the administrative building with the active element storage building behind. (*bottom right*) Charging a nuclear reactor. The workman places uranium capsules in the channels between the graphite of a reactor in the American atomic centre at Oak Ridge.

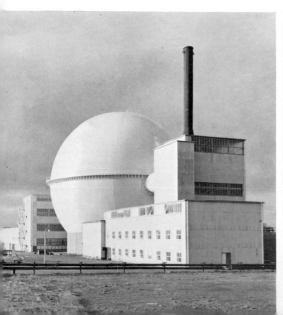

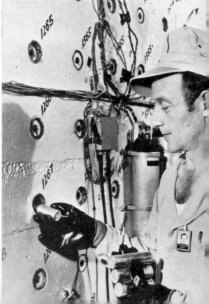

The Netherlands and Norway have worked together for years in the field of the peaceful application of nuclear energy at Kjeller, where the 'Jeep' reactor is situated. We see here the operational panel of 'Jeep' which is already becoming old-fashioned.

(*Below*) For cleaning buildings where radioactive substances are used it is not sufficient to use a vacuum and a mop. Every room is tested periodically with Geiger counters for radioactivity. This photograph was taken at the Windscale plutonium factory. (*right*) 'Hot spaces' are radioactive areas and can only be entered by people wearing protective clothing. The clothing is effective but not flattering.

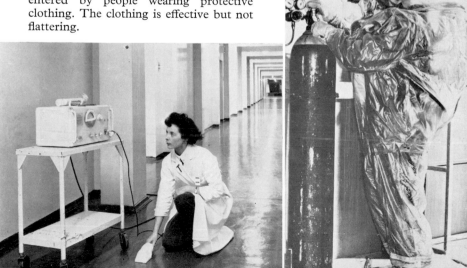

The manufacture of radioactive isotopes requires strict precautions against contamination. Walls of lead blocks always stand between the product and the producer, and they stop most of the radiation. Nevertheless measuring apparatus is kept close at hand, in order to see whether anything irregular is happening. Hygiene is virtually perfect in this sort of laboratory.

(*Below left*) On 17th October, 1956, Queen Elizabeth officially opened the first British and European nuclear power station at Calder Hall. The building containing the reactors is in the centre; on the left are the cooling towers and on the right the turbine houses. The heat liberated by the fission of atomic nuclei is used to transform water into steam, which then drives the turbines. (*below right*) Nuclear reactors do not need to be large, unwieldy and unmanageable—a fact proved by the American atomic submarines and the Russian icebreaker which is driven by nuclear energy. Here is the first American atomic submarine, the *Nautilus*, in Miami Harbour, Florida, on 13th April, 1956.

(*Top left*) This is 'Zeta,' the English apparatus used for investigating nuclear fusion. Initial tests seemed very promising and scholars thought they had succeeded in bringing about nuclear fusion under controlled conditions. Subsequently, they learnt that they had failed. (*top right*) Complicated as the Zeta apparatus may appear to be in practice—the principle is, as this photograph shows, fairly simple. Hot hydrogen gas is ionized in a circular tube and is then brought under the influence of a strong electromagnetic field. It becomes hotter and the current draws the gas towards the centre, so that the walls of the vessel do not vaporize. (*bottom*) The CERN research centre at Geneva. To the left of centre is, half submerged, the circular path of the most powerful protonsynchrotron in existence.

A new nuclear physics laboratory built at Groningen in the Nether-lands in 1959. On the right is the large van de Graaff generator, a linear accelerator, which is built in the high tower of the laboratory. It can produce a potential difference of 5 million volts.

Panic in Putten. This photograph, taken in January 1958, recalls the commotion in the Netherlands when a house in Putten was contaminated with radioactivity. Personnel of the Royal Nether-lands Navy are exami-ning the radioactive stove.

and there is element 93, neptunium, the first artificial element. But the nucleus has still not come to rest. Once again a neutron changes into a proton, an electron is ejected, and behold element 94, plutonium, the second artificial element!

This plutonium is the fissile substance in the atom bomb, for it is just as fissile as U^{235}. The 146 neutrons in U^{238} may well be able to intercept a blow for their 92 protégés, the 145 neutrons in plutonium certainly cannot do that for the 94 protons which are entrusted to their care. In the reactor the unsplittable U^{238} can therefore be transformed into fissile plutonium which can in its turn serve as the fissile material in the nuclear reactor! In other words, by using up fissile material a reactor can manufacture fissile material. And the scholars and technicians are now striving to design a reactor which will make more fissile material than it consumes.

This opens up wide perspectives. Of course the world's supply of uranium and other fissile substances, such as thorium, is very large, but it is pleasant to know that the world's provision of energy will not be directed for ever to $0 \cdot 7\%$ of the supply, but that it will be able to use 100% of it, even if it is by a rather expensive roundabout route.

Also perhaps in time it will be possible to provide our needs of energy without uranium, without the unpleasantness of harmful radiation, without heavy lead nuclear reactors. Possibly one day all our necessary energy will be obtained not from the heaviest, but from the lightest element, namely hydrogen.

There is, after all, already a bomb which works from it. . . .

CHAPTER XII

THE SUN'S SECRET REVEALED. NUCLEAR FUSION: THE NEW
MAGIC WORD. WHAT IS THE PRESENT VIEW ABOUT
PRIMITIVE PARTICLES? A CYCLOTRON IS A SCIENTIFIC
CANNON. WHAT IS THE REAL BASIS OF NATURE?

It must have happened decades ago, on a sunny spring day, one
of those days on which a still somewhat watery sun forces the
wintry cold out of our human bones and on which the birds
suddenly remember that they can sing, a day on which the boys
once again start winking at the girls and the restaurant pro-
prietors hurriedly fill their terraces with tables and chairs—it
must have happened on such a day that a man met a friend who
was looking very worried. 'Don't look so sombre,' he said. 'Is
this a day on which to be worried? Go and sit on a terrace and
let the sun drive away your cares!'

'That's just it, the sun,' answered the friend, who was a
scientist, 'that sun shines and shines, and according to my
calculations it should have ceased to long ago. I don't understand it at all, and that is what is upsetting me.'

This hypothetical scientist on that just as hypothetical fine
spring day decades ago was not the only person who has not
understood anything about the sun. There was in the scientific
and astronomical world no one who could explain what goes on
in the sun and how it comes about that this ball of gas can
radiate enormous amounts of energy in the form of light and
heat for millions of years without completely exhausting itself
and dying. Had we to assume that the sun burns just as a piece
of coal is here on the earth consumed in flames? And, if so, what
burns? For whatever substance was taken—none of them could
supply the enormous amounts of energy which the sun seems
to have at its disposal.

Numerous suppositions have been made and numerous
calculations have been carried out without solving the sun's

secret. The revelation of the mystery was reserved for modern nuclear physics, the science of the atom. The secret is no longer a secret, although it cannot yet be said with certainty that scientists know all they want to know. On the contrary, many details of the processes in the sun are still completely obscure—to use a strange metaphor in this context. The main outlines of the position are however now known. The sun has been shining for 4 or 5 milliard years and it can continue to do so to the same extent for a further many milliards of years. We know how this comes about and we can prophesy fairly accurately what will happen in the future. This explains why scientists can at present sit on a terrace unworried and drink their cups of coffee —at least if it is a fine spring day.

The sun derives its impressive energy from processes in the nuclei of the atoms from which it is constructed. The sun is an enormous nuclear reactor, but it is quite a different reactor from what we know at present on earth. It works in fact in a completely opposite way.

In a nuclear reactor on earth nuclei of heavy atoms are split into nuclei of lighter elements. In the sun atomic nuclei of the lightest element are fused together to form nuclei of a heavier element.

The lightest element—we come once again to the well-known hydrogen—is not famous for nothing, it is, as we have seen, the element from which all substances are in the final analysis built up. And not only that. Of all the matter present in the universe, it has been estimated that a good 55% is hydrogen. The second lightest element, helium, accounts for 44%, and all the other elements form together only 1% of matter. It could be said that the universe consists of hydrogen and helium and that there are here and there slight traces of other elements. The simplest element is the rule in nature, and more complicated substances are exceptions.

The sun also obeys this rule. By far the greatest amount of the matter in the sun is hydrogen, and it is this substance which functions as 'fuel,' or more accurately, it is the nuclei of the hydrogen atoms which serve as a source of energy.

It is hot in the sun, particularly hot, 20 million degrees centigrade at the centre. At this temperature atoms no longer behave normally. The nucleus of the hydrogen atom, consisting of one proton, no longer has one electron rotating nicely in an orbit around it. The electrons have been released and wander about in disorder. The protons do the same. It is absolute chaos in the heart of the sun. Naked hydrogen nuclei shoot about at enormous speeds and sometimes into one another. These speeds are so great that the electrical repulsion between two positively charged nuclei is overcome. Protons collide, penetrate into one another and form all sorts of combinations. The possibilities are many, for example a proton picks up an electron and becomes a neutron, two protons and two neutrons fuse to form a new nucleus. All sorts of nuclear processes are possible, but the final result in our sun is always that nuclei are formed from hydrogen consisting of two protons and two neutrons, in other words, nuclei of helium, the second lightest element. This happens in the sun, helium being formed from hydrogen by means of nuclear fusion. The sun's reactor transforms millions of metric tons of hydrogen into helium every second!

This is consequently the opposite of what happens in our nuclear reactors. There is however one great point of similarity, namely in both cases a very large amount of energy is liberated. What happened during fission? The weight of the products of the fission was less than that of the material from which they had been formed, and this matter was, according to Einstein's equation $E = mc^2$, transformed into energy, into heat. Matter is also lost in the processes taking place in the sun. The helium nucleus which is formed contains less matter than the four hydrogen nuclei forming it. And here too Einstein's comparison is applicable. The matter which is lost is transformed into energy, namely light, heat and other types of radiation. The process of nuclear fusion provides an enormous amount of energy, much more than nuclear fission. Comparatively speaking much more matter is 'lost' during fusion than during fission.

Hydrogen is consequently the 'fuel' of the sun, and helium is the product of the combustion, the 'ash.' 800 million metric tons of hydrogen are transformed into helium every second and that has been going on for a good 4 milliard years. The sun will then slowly be getting towards the end of its strength, and what then? This is not so, however. The sun has so far used up only a few per cent of its hydrogen, and yet so much of it is transformed, millions of metric tons per second. Yes, but there is so much of it!

The sun is by no means yet 'burnt up.' It can still go on for tens of milliards of years—in any case for so long that man need not worry that he will perish because of lack of the sun's energy. Man will have died out long before the sun dies, either by natural causes or by his own doing.

His own doing by hydrogen bombs, for example. Once again we meet hydrogen. For man has copied the sun and has also succeeded in bringing about a nuclear process in which hydrogen is transformed into helium. This was a very difficult task, for the process requires temperatures of a few tens of millions of degrees, and how can they be produced on earth? You get them from the atom bomb, the bomb in which heavy nuclei are split. During the splitting process, which takes place in a fraction of a second, so much heat is liberated that the temperature rises, again for a fraction of a second, to a few tens of millions of degrees. This is very short, but just long enough. If care is taken that a suitable amount of hydrogen is present at the point where this temperature is reached, the fusion reaction begins in the hydrogen of its own accord, and the process also takes place in the fraction of a second.

That then is the hydrogen bomb, a bomb which is filled with hydrogen—for technical reasons with a mixture of the heavy isotopes deuterium and tritium—and which is set going by a percussion cap, consisting of an 'ordinary' atom bomb.

Do not ask what this weapon costs. If we think about this, we shall soon shake our heads dejectedly, but the military authorities seem to be at great pains to have a weapon which can destroy mankind in its entirety. Nuclear physicists are much more modest. They would merely like to have sufficient means to realize their latest dream, namely to bring about nuclear fusion not in an explosive manner, as in the bomb, but gradually and in a controlled way, just as the fission process in reactors takes place under control.

If great difficulties were involved in the development of controlled nuclear fission, they are simply enormous in the case of controlled nuclear fusion. Experts expect that it will be about twenty years before we can control the fusion process completely and that it will certainly not be before the end of this century that this process will be made suitable for economic use.

Why must we then necessarily indulge in nuclear fusion? We now have nuclear fission, and look at the energy that produces! Yes, but nuclear fission is really very troublesome. In the first place we need materials for it which can be obtained only at very great cost from the earth. Then these substances are, even if in reasonable supply, not available in unlimited amounts. And in the third place nuclear fission is accompanied by dangerous radioactive radiation which renders expensive protective steps necessary, so that the reactors are unwieldy.

We may, of course, be thankful that nuclear fission has become possible just at the time when the world's supplies of oil and coal, which have been used up till now, threaten to become exhausted. We shall however in due course undoubtedly welcome controlled nuclear fusion with open arms and relegate fission to the museum with our thanks for the services it has rendered. For the supply of 'fuel' for nuclear fusion on the earth is inexhaustible—it is water. And the process of fusion does not cause any mentionable radioactivity. Just think of the great significance of this point!

Nuclear fusion is the new magic word of scholars and technicians. Work is proceeding in many countries—including our own—to break open this treasure-house which will provide man with all the energy he requires, however much that may be.

Up till now we have not yet succeeded in bringing about controlled fusion. Everywhere enormous apparatus consume tremendous amounts of electricity, technicians sit at drawing-boards and physicists are experimenting with electric currents and magnetic fields. What is the difficulty? The temperature!

For producing and sustaining the fusion reaction a temperature of many millions of degrees is needed, while all terrestrial substances are vaporized at a few thousand degrees. How then shall we ever be able to construct a device in which nuclear fusion can be carried out? Man is cunning. If nature leaves him even the slightest possibility, he will not fail to make use of it. And in the case of nuclear fusion there is such a slight possibility.

We saw that in the sun the hydrogen nuclei, that is the protons, are robbed of their electrons. They are, as it is called, ionized and are no longer electrically neutral, but have a positive charge. If we therefore ionize hydrogen, we obtain a gas with a positive electrical charge and it is subject to attraction by negative electricity and sensitive to magnetism. Here is the chance on which scholars and technicians have pinned their hopes.

An amount of ionized hydrogen is taken and is heated in a vessel by passing an electric current through it. The gas is however not only heated, but is at the same time attracted by the current which runs right through the vessel. If the current is so powerful that all the gas is attracted to the centre of the vessel while it is at the same time heated to a very high temperature, both by the current and the contraction, then the walls of the vessel are protected against overheating since the gas does not then touch them.

Technicians have already succeeded in this way in producing temperatures of a few million degrees for an extremely short period, but those temperatures have not been high enough for sufficiently long to cause fusion. A few years ago, the English thought they had succeeded with their famous 'Zeta' apparatus, but further investigations showed that they had been wrong.

But this is not yet all, for even if we succeed in bringing about fusion in this way, there is still a long way to go. It is not merely a matter of causing fusion; that will certainly be possible when enough electrical energy is expended on it and when a solution is found to a number of technological problems. It is however a question of bringing about nuclear fusion in such a way that the fusion reaction sustains itself and consequently releases more energy than has to be expended to start the process! If this is successful, then the richest treasure-store of nature will have been opened up for man. Whether and, if so, in what way this will be possible, we dare not prophesy.

But if it is successful, there will in the course of the next century rise up everywhere in the world electrical power-stations which will work by nuclear fusion, which will obtain the raw material for their fusion reactors from water and which will provide current in enormous amounts at a minimum price. Then it will be possible to transform deserts into fertile plains, there will be plenty of food and clothing for all mankind, innumerable industrial products will be able to be brought on to the market at prices within everyone's reach, then there will be everything, unless explosive nuclear fusion renders all science superfluous. The least we can require is however that the rulers of this world will be able to control themselves.

We cannot imagine, nor could even a modern Jules Verne, what concrete possibilities will have been realized by nuclear fusion in, let us say, 200 years. Probably it will have changed the face of the earth completely. Even now modern science has brought about radical changes in almost all fields of life, and we are living only on the threshold of tomorrow.

Modern science is just at the beginning of its development. We still know precious little about the processes in the atomic nucleus, and much study and experimenting will be needed before we can penetrate farther into the mysteries of nature.

To give just one example in this wide field, what are the basic particles of matter really like?

We are already making industrial and economic use of protons, electrons, neutrons, but what is their nature? Are they the basic particles? It was formerly thought that atoms were the constructional units of matter. Is it now thought that these are the protons and electrons?

The farther we penetrate into the atom, the more confusing the situation becomes. There are in fact various 'basic particles,' such as protons, electrons, neutrons, positrons, antiprotons, mesons, neutrinos, hyperons, in all some thirty of them—so far. Is this not in conflict with the essence of nature, which gives preference to simplicity? Could not all these different particles with all their different properties be different forms of one or two genuine basic particles?

This is a problem which is engaging the cleverest brains. At the Second Atoms for Peace Conference of the United Nations, held in Geneva in 1958, a report was discussed which expressed very cautiously the assumption that protons are not, after all, the fundamental constructional units of the universe. There are indications that protons are not simple, but complex, for it could be that they have a given structure, at least according to the extremely cautious terms of this report. If this is so, then the question arises as to whether protons are constructed in one way or another, as yet unknown to us, from particles we know, or whether they consist of particles of a much smaller order.

More simply, could a proton, for example, consist of three, four or a hundred mesons, or could it be made up from a few quadrillion much smaller particles, just as the sun consists of several quadrillion protons?

Perhaps the enormous synchrotrons, bevatrons, cosmotrons and other accelerating devices, which are coming more and more into use, will once again give an indication of the direction in which the solution must be sought.

Yes, that cyclotron is really an apparatus with which man can get to work on nature. It is a device which may be regarded as a scientific cannon. Let us examine it more closely.

CHAPTER XIII

MODERN RESEARCH ON NUCLEAR PHYSICS. UNITED EUROPE
HAS AN 'ATOMIC RACE-COURSE.' LAWRENCE'S DISCOVERY—
THE LIFE'S WORK OF ADAMS. MORE THAN MILLIONS AND
MILLIARDS OF ELECTRON-VOLTS

If we wish to study the apparatus which is called by the complicated word 'synchrocyclotron,' we shall do best to go to Geneva,
for the most powerful apparatus in the world has been operating
there since the beginning of 1960, being the property of twelve
European countries.

If someone pressed the sum of £10 million into your hand
telling you to design and build with it the largest and most
powerful synchrocyclotron in the world, then you would
probably scratch your head and think for a moment. No doubt
the English nuclear physicist, J. B. Adams, did that several times
as he sat behind his drawing-board after he was commissioned
with this task, for it was a gigantic job and Adams was in the
first instance responsible for it. We cannot say even approximately how many difficulties the young Englishman had to
solve, how much calculating and drawing had to be done. The
result was, in any case, that twelve European countries now
jointly possess the most powerful particle accelerator in the
world and have in this way gained a considerable start on the
United States and the Soviet Union as far as scientific research
on the nature of matter is concerned.

This 'atomic race-course' of United Europe is situated at the
border between Switzerland and France, in Meyrin, near
Geneva. Experts from all countries jostle one another there for
the maximum of ingenuity and technical ability amongst
modern scholars. This 'race-course' has the official name of
'25 GeV protonsynchrotron of the European Organization for
Research in Nuclear Physics' and was officially opened in

February 1960 by the great Danish scientist and Nobel Prize winner, Professor Niels Bohr.

Now £10 million is no trifle, but the twelve countries which have jointly made this sum available have a total of 460 million inhabitants, so that the apparatus has in reality not cost more than about 6d. per head of the population of United Europe. That is really a very modest amount when we consider the wide prospects which are opened up at Meyrin. It may almost be said that the cost is negligible compared with the enormous scientific importance of the apparatus, which may be called the life's work of Adams, the former director, and his colleagues.

The *scientific* importance, this is what is continually stressed by the people at CERN, as the organization is called according to its French abbreviation (Conseil Européen pour la Recherche Nucléaire). Their greatest fear is that misunderstandings should arise concerning the nature of their work. They have nothing to do—and do not want to have anything to do—with the practical applications of nuclear physics, whether they be military or peaceful. Atom bombs and nuclear power stations are matters from which they dissociate themselves. CERN carries out pure scientific research without bothering about the question as to whether that work will ever yield practical results and, if so, which. In Meyrin an attempt is being made to force from nature her deepest secrets and to penetrate into the mysterious domain of the extremely small, namely the atomic nucleus, the elementary particles, the relationships, effects and all the rest which determine the properties of the microcosm. In short, scientists are doing no more than satisfying their thirst for knowledge, just as Faraday for the same reason once sat playing with wires and coils without supposing that his 'game' would one day result in the enormously extended use of electricity.

They do not play with wires and coils at CERN, they work with an enormous circular apparatus, 200 metres in diameter, in which protons are given a very high velocity so that they can be used as projectiles for bombarding other atomic nuclei.

That bombarding of atomic nuclei has—as we have already seen—been the favourite occupation of nuclear physicists for the last few decades. It is, after all, one of the very few methods for discovering something about the secrets of the world of the atom. Since Lord Rutherford was the first to make one element from another by means of bombardment, scientific 'shooting galleries' have been set up all over the world.

We have already referred in a previous chapter to the work of Rutherford, Joliot and Curie and others. We must now examine it more closely. What did they do? They directed the radiation from a radioactive substance at an element they wished to transform. Looked at closely, that was however by no means as clear as it appeared from a distance, for what scientists did at that time was to experiment a bit in the dark. When they directed the rays from radium at a target, it was really as if they were firing a cannon, without aiming, on the North Sea coast in the hope of hitting a whale somewhere along the Dutch coast. If by this bombardment they did hit a nucleus, then it was a chance hit. In the first place the nucleus occupies only a very small part of the total space taken up by the atom, and, secondly, both the projectiles and the goals had a positive electric charge, so that they repelled one another, while the velocity of most projectiles was inadequate to overcome that repulsive force. The yield of the bombardments was therefore frankly pitiful. Something had to be done about it. The means which nature provided were not sufficient, the projectiles were unaimed, too small in number and too slow. Man had, therefore, once again to give nature a helping hand, better and more efficient cannons had to be found.

Scientists with a technical bent—officially called experimental physicists—attacked the problem from all sides. And they succeeded.

Transcendent electricity was here again to be the saviour in the time of need, for since they were electrically charged, the protons and alpha particles were subject to electrical repulsion and attraction. Scientists therefore reasoned that, if an electrical tension were aroused between two poles and if their projectiles were brought between those poles, they would be repulsed by the positive and attracted by the negative pole, that is to say, they would move from one to the other, and if the tension were made high enough, they could give the projectiles just that velocity they wanted to—and then they would be finished.

They were in fact finished—at least for the moment, for particularly high tensions appeared to be necessary, and very soon techniques were found to be at fault. Potential differences of hundreds of thousands of volts seemed possible, even those up to a few million volts could be produced by technicians. But when they rubbed their hands with pleasure at their achievements, the physicists shook their heads with annoyance. The projectiles were by no means yet rich enough in energy for their liking. A proton which had passed through a potential difference of a million volts had an energy of 1 million electron-volts, an alpha particle could, after such an adventure, boast of an energy of 2 million electron-volts—it has twice the charge of a proton —but what is that compared, for example, with the cosmic radiation which reaches our earth on all sides from space and in which there are particles with energies of tens of milliards of electron-volts? If we could only produce such energies, then the atomic nucleus could really be attacked. But the gentlemen looked at one another questioningly. Who can produce tensions of milliards of volts?

At that moment a young American came forward with the egg of Columbus. Ernest Lawrence put an end to the problem of the extremely high tensions by inventing an apparatus which had approximately the same shape as the famous egg, being round. Lawrence discovered the cyclotron, an achievement which gained for him the Nobel Prize for physics in 1939.

Apart from being sensitive to electricity, charged particles are also sensitive to magnetism, and this is a scientific fact of which Lawrence made extremely ingenious use. He built a circular device in which he forced the protons to describe a circular path by means of magnetic fields. On two sides of the round box he applied an alternating electric current. And behold, a proton was attracted by the one and repulsed by the other pole, and consequently moved towards the former, but found with horror that at the moment of arrival the tension was altered, so that it was now repulsed and attracted by the pole it had just left. The proton found no peace, again and again as it reached an attracting pole, that pole became repulsive and again and again it thereby got a nasty blow in the back. The result was that, as time went on, it circled faster and faster until Lawrence took pity on it and released the proton from the race-course by means of a trick, and used it as a projectile, being grateful for its high velocity.

At first the inventor himself had little trust in the success of his experiment. Yet the faster a particle moves, the more rapidly it describes its orbit—it would therefore soon be 'out of step' with the alternating current. Fortunately this did not turn out to be the case. For the faster a particle moves, the farther it is forced towards the edge of the box by the centrifugal force, and the longer its path therefore becomes. All particles, whether fast or slow, rotate in the same time, being continually urged on by the alternating tension. With his first proper cyclotron Lawrence reached an energy of 16 million electron-volts with an alternating current of 100,000 volts. He also had just as many projectiles as he wanted, and he could also aim them accurately at the goal.

In 1930 Lawrence demonstrated his first cyclotron. He was then twenty-nine. Since then accelerating devices have been built at many places in the world, in the United States, England, the Soviet Union, France, the Netherlands, in short, almost everywhere where nuclear physicists live and work. The cyclotrons, bevatrons, cosmotrons and whatever else they may be called have become steadily larger and more complicated. The energies obtained have also become higher and higher, 50 million, 100 million, 200 million electron-volts. Protons and alpha particles now circulate around everywhere. They change elements into other elements, make new elements, affect photographic plates and bring new particles to light.

Cyclotrons are becoming more and more immense and complicated . . . and expensive. A number of years ago the governments of twelve European countries decided to do together what they could no longer do individually. They founded the European Organization for Research in Nuclear Physics, the present director of which is Dr. V. F. Weisskopf from Vienna. Within a few years this organization achieved what had previously been considered impossible. Weary old Europe caught up not only the United States and the Soviet Union, but even gained a lead in the field of basic physical research on these young, energetic countries with their rich resources.

Now American and Russian scholars can, if they wish, come and carry out experiments in Geneva, which they cannot (yet) carry out in their own countries. The door is open to everyone, for this purely scientific research does not accept any secrecy and discrimination.

Those who now wander about CERN recognize only the form of the first primitive apparatus of Lawrence, the circular course for protons, half underground, 200 metres in diameter, that is to say 628 metres in circumference, which took six years to build. In a linear pre-accelerator the protons acquire an energy of 50 million electron-volts. In the course itself they afterwards rotate at a rate of 480,000 times a second, as a result of which their energy is increased to 25 *milliard* electron-volts and their speed to 99·94% of that of light, this being 180 kilometres per second below the 300,000 kilometres per second of light! 10 milliard protons race round per second. A bombardment with this stream of protons has virtually the same effect on matter as an intense cosmic radiation. It is therefore to be expected that CERN will also be able to unravel many secrets of this, in many ways, still mysterious type of radiation.

In Chapter VIII we noted in passing that in the construction of cyclotrons account must be taken of the phenomena of relativity. We said there that the devices are called *synchro*trons because they are synchronized for the relative increase in mass. It can be imagined that this increase in mass must be quite distinct in the accelerator belonging to CERN, in which the protons reach no less than 99·94% of the speed of light. This is the case. The protons which are accelerated to an energy of 25 milliard electron-volts appear to leave the apparatus with a mass which is twenty-five times greater than their mass at rest! There could hardly be finer proof of the correctness of the theory of relativity.

We as outsiders cannot form any idea of the unbelievable technical refinement involved in building the protonsynchrotron. Just imagine the complicated connections which are necessary to change the direction of an electric current, not fifty times a second—as in our domestic system—but a few hundred thousand times a second. Perhaps you will get some idea of the complicated nature of this masterpiece of technical work if you consider that the remote control of the apparatus alone, necessary because of the radioactivity, required 3,600 kilometres of wire and cable . . . the magnets weighing several tons, not to mention the degree of precision which had to be taken into account in the construction (over 200 metres accurate to half a *milli*metre!), and all the other achievements of the Europeans who worked together on this project.

Yes, J. B. Adams will certainly have scratched his head before everything was cut and dried. And now that the protons are whirling round, he will certainly not rest on his laurels, for the real scientific work is just about to begin.

Using all his ingenuity man is investigating nature, using the synchrotron at Geneva, the ordinary microscope, mathematical formulae, expensive spectroscopes. He is seeking the essence of nature. It is his tragedy that he will never find what he is, in the final analysis, seeking.

For a question will have suggested itself even to the reader of this book. He has now read about cyclotrons and nuclear reactors, about planets and galaxies, about $E = mc^2$ and the curved time-space continuum, about electrons and radio-activity. We are beginning to approach the end of our journey through modern science. We have described how all manner of things behave, how they give evidence of their presence, what relationships exist between them. But the reader will feel dissatisfied if he considers the matter further, for he will ask himself, what *are* things really like, what is the *essence* of nature?

That question has so far been avoided for a reason. Science cannot provide the answer, either now or in the future. The only consolation she offers us is that she can tell us why the answer can never be given.

CHAPTER XIV

A FAIRY TALE ABOUT MAN. THE NATURE OF THINGS IS
IMPENETRABLE. WHAT IS LIGHT? ONLY AVERAGES CAN BE
USED. MACROCOSM AND MICROCOSM: HAS HEISENBERG
FOUND THE GREAT SYNTHESIS?

A Fairy Tale

There was once a very strange being. It consisted merely of
eyes and brains and it lived near a long and high wall. Its eyes
were fixed on that wall—it always had to look at it, it knew
nothing other than that wall. The wall was its whole world, and
what took place on that wall the being could analyse and
interpret with its brains. It was certainly a very strange creature.

A long way from the wall, behind the creature, stood a strong
lamp which illuminated the wall. And people moved between
the lamp on the one hand and the creature and the wall on the
other. The creature could not see those people, it saw only their
shadows on the wall. It had, of course, no idea of what people
are in reality like, but by perceiving what happened on the wall,
that is to say in its world, it could however form a very accurate
picture. It could, for example, ascertain that man does not have
a fixed size, but can make himself very large and very small at
will. It also found that man does not have any definite, fixed form,
but can assume all sorts of forms arbitrarily. A third observation taught it that one man can completely fuse with another
man, can be completely absorbed and can again free himself.

The creature's observations were exact. No one would have
needed to try to point out that it had the wrong end of the stick.
Its measurements and observations did not admit of any other
interpretation.

The creature could not turn round, fixed as it was facing the
wall. If it had been able to, it would have been extremely
surprised to see that its seemingly so real observations and
accurate calculations did not agree at all with reality. It would,

for example, have seen that man certainly does have a given size, but that his shadow on the wall becomes larger as he moves away from the wall towards the lamp, and smaller if he does the opposite. It would have seen that man certainly has a fixed, given outline, but that he can turn and move so that his shadow can assume all sorts of forms. It would finally have found that man cannot be absorbed into a congener, but can let his silhouette coincide with that of another person by going and standing behind or in front of that person.

The creature would have formed quite a different picture of reality if it had not been so restricted in its powers that it was relying solely on silhouettes on a wall.

A fairy tale?

Not completely, for man's position as regards nature is like that of the creature as regards the phenomenon of man. Because his powers are limited, man cannot perceive nature as it is—he must be contented with the silhouettes which can be perceived by his fixed gaze. However ingenious and accurate human observations and calculations may be—man will never be able to 'turn round' and see how things really are. Reality will be very different from what man can ever imagine.

We were able to see this when we were discussing the curved four-dimensional time-space continuum. We can discover it once again if we start answering an apparently very simple question in order to illustrate our assertions, namely what is light and how is it formed?

If we put this question to a physicist, he will apparently give an accurate and correct answer, namely that light is an electro-magnetic vibration of a certain wavelength, and that it arises when in an atom an electron jumps from a given orbit to one which is closer to the nucleus, thereby emitting the resultant excess of energy in the form of an electromagnetic vibration. The physicist cannot say more than that. If we persist, then he will write down a few formulae and point to them. These are the formulae of the great physicists Max Planck and Niels Bohr. Yet, even assuming that the questioner is so well trained in mathematics that he can understand these formulae, does all this answer his question?

No, the scientist has merely said *how* nature does it and not what nature does. He has merely described the external phenomenon. To the question as to how a clock works, he has merely answered what time it is.

It is worth investigating more deeply the question of the nature of light, precisely because here the 'silhouettes' are so clear.

Rutherford taught that in the atom electrons describe orbits around the nucleus, but he said nothing more about the nature of those orbits. This was done by the Danish scientist, Niels Bohr, one of his pupils. Bohr explained that the orbits of the electrons are not arbitrary, as is the orbit of the earth around the sun. The earth could, on an average, rotate a million miles nearer to or farther from the sun without making any change in the principles of the solar system. This is not the case with the atom, according to Bohr. Each electron has a very definite orbit and must stick to it. It can pass from one orbit to the other; for example, from the orbit which is closest to the nucleus into the second one which is somewhat farther away. It does not do that gradually, by describing a 'spiral' motion around it, but by a jump. It moves suddenly from one orbit to the other. That does not, however, happen automatically. The electron is electrically attracted by the nucleus, and energy has therefore to be used to bring it from the first to the second path, in order to 'shift' it. The electron then follows the second path, for a millionth of a second or thereabouts. Nature prefers the simplest state and rapidly restores it. The electron therefore quickly jumps back into the first orbit, and this takes place with milliards of electrons millions of times a second. Each time it springs back the energy is liberated which was used to 'shift' the electron. Irrespective of the form in which that energy was added, the electron knows only one way of returning it, namely in the form of an electromagnetic vibration, the wavelength of which is determined by the orbits between which the electron has jumped, this being a vibration which man calls 'light.'

This has all been worked out carefully and confirmed experimentally. Each orbit of electrons around the nucleus appeared to represent a given energy value, and it was possible to derive from the nature of the atom what kind of light it would radiate. Sodium, for example, turned out to emit yellow light.

Had science therefore explained what light is like? Not at all, for it has not been able to say what exactly happens when an atom emits light. First there is an amount of excess energy, later there is light of a given wavelength. But how does this transformation come about? We cannot perceive precisely what nature does. We see no more than a silhouette of reality. That jumping of electrons is very nice, but it is nothing more than a shadow of what really happens.

We must penetrate a little more deeply into this matter, for the gymnastic turns of the electrons have an effect on the phenomenon of light. At the beginning of this century Max Planck had established that light is not an uninterrupted flow, but consists of separate 'parcels,' called quanta. The propagation of light cannot be compared with the emptying of a bucket of water, but with the turning upside down of a box of pebbles. The quanta appeared to be able to behave like particles of matter. They could propagate themselves through an empty space, they could exert pressure on materials. Not only light, but all forms of electromagnetic energy appeared to consist of quanta, of 'atoms of energy' we might say. The size of the quanta was not always the same, but appeared to depend on the wavelength. The light quanta were given a name of their own, namely photons.

This phenomenon of the quantum appeared to be closely related to the jumps of electrons. An electron is seized by a quantum of energy and on falling back returns a photon. Each individual electron therefore produces an individual amount of energy, namely the amount which it has left. Light is therefore a collection of individual amounts of energy, it consists of fragments of all types.

Does this explain light? What happens continues to be impenetrable. The atom is still a mysterious apparatus to us, amounts of energy pass in at one side and photons come out at the other. Light cannot be 'explained' in the deepest sense of the word.

This becomes clearer still when we look more closely at that individual electron we have just been talking about. What is an individual electron? Can we see, study and analyse it? No, it is much too small for that, and it moves far too quickly as well. Good, but what if we now assume that it is possible to construct a microscope which will magnify so much that it could make an electron visible? That will still not be of any assistance, for in order to be able to see the electron, we must illuminate it, a quantum of energy must be cast upon it; but that does not leave the electron unaffected! The quantum has an effect on the electron and disturbs the normal course of events. In other words, the fact that we wish to observe, disturbs what we want to observe. 'Looking' is therefore impossible, at least looking very accurately. The observations are accurate up to a certain limit. If we go beyond that, we must begin to take account of very serious errors due to the fact that we are interfering with the process being observed by the very fact of our observation. The German scientist, Professor Dr. W. Heisenberg, laid this down many years ago in a formula, which is called the 'uncertainty principle.' This rule defines the limits of human ability to find out what happens in the world of extremely small objects. Man cannot possibly say what one given electron is going to do in the next second. The behaviour and the properties of an 'individual electron' cannot therefore be determined.

Scientists have therefore also turned away from the individual electron—they cannot do anything with it. They have attacked the matter in another way, in the way in which, for example, a life insurance company works.

Such a company works with averages. An English company when determining its premiums investigates the age to which the *average* Englishman lives. Let us say that it is seventy-five years. If someone wants to insure himself, then the company, when deciding the insurance premium, starts from the principle that the candidate will live to seventy-five, at least if his health is normal and he does not live an abnormally dangerous life. There is a reasonable chance that the man will not live to seventy-five, but only to forty-nine or perhaps even to ninety-eight. If it is a question of an old-age pension, then the company has gained in the first case and has had a heavy loss in the second. That does not matter to it, for it is not dealing with this man alone. It has more than ten, perhaps a hundred thousand insured persons. And taken over the whole group, the gains will outweigh the losses, so that the company will on the whole come out well. The company therefore maintains data which are wrong for almost every individual, but which are none the less completely correct for a very large group of individuals taken as a whole.

Scientists deal in this way with things which escape their observations individually, but which are present in enormous numbers. They fix averages, and we can see how accurate these are when we consider that, for example, the whole of 'electronics' is based thereon, and provides results such as television sets, electron microscopes and the like, which are miracles of precision.

The statistical method is the only possible one in modern science. One can work only with averages and must disregard the real behaviour of individual things. Physicists are not concerned with a separate quantum of energy, a photon, an electron, an atom. They work with billions and trillions of them. They are making do with silhouettes; the reality behind them does not interest them, because they cannot approach it. They leave that reality to the philosophers. Yet in the last few decades they have been getting closer and closer to reality. Whatever subject we choose, we see that man has approached the limit of his powers, that he has accurately analysed the silhouettes of reality and that there is not much remaining except that final step, the 'turning round'—the step which man will never be able to take, because he in fact lacks the material, and particularly the spiritual powers to do so.

Scientists have become very well aware of this, particularly as they have penetrated into the great field covered by the general name 'radioactivity.' In this field too, there is a magnificent example of the application of statistical methods, which is of great importance for modern life and which is therefore worthy of closer attention.

The element uranium is, as we have already seen, radioactive. Again and again an atom perishes in a given amount of this substance; it emits radiations and thus changes into another element. Why do not all atoms behave like this? They are all precisely the same—why does one atom disintegrate now, while its neighbour will not do so for five or five thousand years? Who or what determines which atom is to be next? Nobody has any idea. All that is known is that, in an amount of radioactive material, one atom will immediately disintegrate. Human knowledge cannot say why just that one atom disintegrates, while trillions of identical atoms in its immediate vicinity continue to exist. We cannot in this case examine the individual atoms. Here a suitable average has again been sought, and this has been found in the what is called the 'half-value period.'

The half-value period is the time in which half the number of atoms in a given amount of radioactive material has decayed. Uranium has a half-value period of $4\frac{1}{2}$ milliard years. This means that 1 kilogramme of uranium will after $4\frac{1}{2}$ milliard years have become $0 \cdot 5$ kilogramme. Of that remaining 500 grammes, 250 grammes will be left after a further $4\frac{1}{2}$ milliard years, and after a further equal period of time there will be 125 grammes, and so on, until eventually the very last atom will have succumbed to its fate.

The half-value period is a very useful magnitude, since each radioactive element maintains its own period. Radium, for example, has a half-value period of 1,580 years, thorium one of 20 milliard years, radium C (a product of decay), on the other hand, has one of a millionth of a second. An element can therefore be identified on the basis of the half-value period. This is very useful in cases where we have so little of a substance that it cannot be analysed chemically, or if its period of existence is so short that there is just no time for chemical analysis.

The statistical value of the half-value period also appears to be of unique importance in everyday matters. Archaeologists, for example, are thrilled by it, just as are doctors, agriculturalists, industrialists and many other people active in other fields.

Let us just take a short journey into the field of archaeology.

Carbon occurs in the air in a gaseous compound with oxygen which is called carbon dioxide (CO_2). This carbon dioxide is absorbed by plants and trees. The carbon is kept by the organism and is used for building it up. As with all the other elements, there are isotopes of carbon. The isotope C^{12} is the normal one, constituting more than 98% of all the carbon occurring in nature. This is a perfectly normal substance without radioactivity or anything else. But alongside it in the atmosphere there is also present in a very slight amount a radioactive isotope, namely C^{14}. This arises through nitrogen atoms—which constitute about 80% of the air—being struck by powerful cosmic radiation. The nitrogen nuclei are transformed by this bombardment into carbon nuclei. Amongst the molecules of CO_2 in the atmosphere, there are those in which there is C^{14} in place of C^{12}. But seeing that carbon is carbon, plants and trees do not make any distinction and the C^{14} is therefore 'treated' normally. Once it has been absorbed by the plant organism, it undergoes precisely the same process as C^{12}. C^{14} is however not stable. In common with all radioactive substances, it decays according to an immutable half-value period. This fact is of great importance for archaeologists. After all, as long as a plant lives C^{12} plus C^{14} are absorbed in a fixed ratio. If the organism dies, then the absorption of carbon ceases. What however continues is the decay of C^{14}. That means that the longer the organism has been dead the more the ratio between C^{12} and C^{14} in the remains will continue to alter. On the basis of the half-value period of C^{14} and of its amount in the dead organic remains, a calculation can therefore be made as to how long ago the plant or tree died! And that is not all. Animals and man eat plant and animal food, and the C^{14} is also absorbed into their bones, so that their age can be determined. With the help of the 'C^{14} method,' scientists have succeeded in determining the age of pieces of wood from the Egyptian pyramids and consequently how long ago these buildings were erected. This method is not accurate to one year, because the measuring apparatus for radioactive decay cannot be refined indefinitely. But on average the determinations of age are accurate to a few hundred years!

A second example of the use of the half-value period lies in the determination of the age of the earth itself. At places where radioactive substances occur in the ground, the decay products of these substances are also found. We can determine the ratio between the two and then calculate, on the basis of the half-value period, how long ago it was that the substances were placed there. This is however a field with so many pitfalls that we will give it wide berth.

Archaeologists and geologists are consequently very pleased about radioactive isotopes. But let us not forget ourselves! These substances also play a very important part in medicine and they can at present mean the difference between life and death for us. By serving a patient a radioactive material, we can investigate very accurately how his organism reacts to it, how it processes the substance and where the disturbances lie. Yet radioactivity can be dangerous. We must therefore determine very accurately how long the—in any case weak—radioactivity must last in order to provide the required information. If that is a day, then the doctor can choose a half-value period such that after twenty-four hours all the radioactive atoms will have decayed. If the measurement has to last two weeks, then a substance with a different half-value period can be chosen, although the choice is naturally very strongly limited by the fact that not every substance can be chosen for any organ. Thus, for thyroid examination, we are virtually directed to radioactive iodine.

Yet, in general, the half-value period enables man to use radioactivity to the correct extent, for the correct period and in the correct manner!

Here too the 'silhouettes' of reality, the statistical averages, are consequently of the greatest accuracy and usefulness.

Yes, in spite of the limited nature of his powers, man has achieved much. He thought that too, as we have already explained, at the end of the previous century, but in quite a different way. At that time those engaged in science considered they would one day be in a position to unmask all the laws of nature and to explain everything. Now scholars know that they will never be able to go beyond a more or less complete *description* of the behaviour of nature and that the essence which lurks behind this will never be revealed to them.

A *description* of nature, not an *explanation*. Will science ever complete that description? And how will it describe everything?

There will certainly never be a question of finishing, because behind every phenomenon which is captured in scientific language there loom up new phenomena which require description. What is the position with the bases of everything?

It looks as if those bases can in fact be adequately described in mathematical symbols. This sentence contains at the same time the answer to the question as to how scientists want to describe everything. For the scientist, it is a question of approaching the phenomena in nature in such a way that he describes the maximum number of facts with the minimum possible number of assumptions. If two outwardly totally different things can be covered by one and the same formula, then there must be an internal similarity. The brilliant Einstein won great merit by 'covering' a very large number of phenomena in nature in only a few formulae. It appeared from his work that

137

there exists in nature a great harmony, a synthesis, which can be characterized in mathematical language but the essence of which—let us repeat it—escapes us.

Yet the harmony, the synthesis is prejudiced because nature appeared to have a twofold character. No formula could be found which described both electromagnetic and gravitational phenomena. Both types of phenomena appear to resemble one another very much. Their basic comparisons have precisely the same mathematical form, yet—microcosm and macrocosm, the extremely small and the extremely large, could not be brought together in one formula which would cause them to emerge as one tremendous unity, from which all their diversity could be described. For thirty years Einstein sought for what he called the 'general field theory.'

Is the universe a unity? Could one, starting from one mathematical formula, describe everything from the behaviour of electrons to that of galaxies, from the curvature of space to the decay of radioactive elements? Or would nature be hermaphroditic, would the macrocosm differ essentially from the microcosm?

$$\gamma_\upsilon \frac{d}{dx}\upsilon\,\psi + \ell^2\,\gamma_\mu\,\gamma_5\,\psi\,(\,\psi^+\gamma_\mu\gamma_5\psi) = 0$$

Heisenberg's formula—the great synthesis?

The answer appears to have been found by Professor Dr. Werner Heisenberg, one of the most outstanding German scholars at the moment. He appears to have found what Einstein was looking for, namely the great synthesis. He has established a formula from which all the known laws of nature, both of the microcosm and of the macrocosm, appear to be able to be derived.

This is not yet certain. The mathematical testing of it will require a very long time, and much theoretical and experimental work will be required before certainty is obtained.

If Heisenberg has in fact succeeded in his aim, science will have advanced very much farther, for apart from all that is already known acquiring a new clarification, much that is unknown will be cleared up.

Nature one great harmonious whole, the macrocosm being in essence the same as the microcosm. This as yet unproven supposition entices us to consider possibilities at which we become dizzy. The atom a solar system. A solar system with life? Life that completes itself in what we call a milliardth part of a second? And compared with this, our solar system . . . an atom? An atom in a super-world, in which a milliardth part of a second is what we call millions of years, a super world with life?

Let us not pursue this path further. These are the fancies of a layman, about which science is not concerned, and we wish to limit ourselves to science in this book. It will be better, now that this book is approaching its end, to concern ourselves once again with the beginning.

Nature a great harmonious whole. How has it become what it is? Has the universe always existed, or did it come into existence? Was there a beginning or not? And will there be an end?

CHAPTER XV

BEGINNING AND END . . . OR ETERNITY? GAMOW AND
HOYLE DISAGREE ENTIRELY. MAN WILL NOT SEE THE SUN
DIE. NONE THE LESS, WE SHALL LIVE A LONG TIME IF WE
ARE SENSIBLE

There was once a king who wanted to know how long eternity lasts. He asked his nobles, but they did not know. He asked his court jester, but he passed it off with a joke. He asked the Council of Forty, which included the oldest and wisest men in the country, but the Council could not give an answer. Dejectedly, the king had his horse saddled and, disheartened, he rode away from the palace in order to be alone with nature and to try to find the answer himself. But behold, on his journey he met a simple shepherd's boy who was grazing a flock. The king also asked him if he knew how long eternity lasts. 'Majesty,' went the answer, 'in the East, a long way from here, there is a mountain of pure diamond, a thousand metres long, a thousand metres wide and a thousand metres high. Once in every thousand years a small bird comes to sharpen its beak on that mountain. When the whole mountain is worn away by that sharpening, one second of eternity will have passed.'

This is, in brief, the contents of one of the many magnificent eastern fairy tales in which the wisdom of whole races is incorporated for those who take the trouble to seek it out. Time and eternity are matters which are mentioned in them many times in many forms.

The sober branches of sciences do not have anything to do with eastern fairy tales, but nevertheless have to consider closely the question of time and eternity. They do not do this by thinking about diamonds, mountains and small birds, but by cool reasoning based on mathematical data and objective observations. The question which they seek to answer is: 'Is the universe, or that small part of it which man can observe, temporary or eternal?' There is a special branch of knowledge which is concerned with answering this question and which has been given the name 'cosmogony.'

Cosmogony is just at the very beginning of its development. Of course the question of the origin of all things has interested man as long as he has existed, but only in the last few decades has the knowledge and ability of man reached the level at which it has been possible to attempt to investigate the history of the universe on an objective basis and by scientific methods. Cosmogony received one of its most important impulses from the discoveries of Einstein, whose work had a very great influence on the whole of science. During the last few years however a development has been discernible which suggests that young scholars wish to proceed along their own paths, even if these do not run parallel with those taken by Einstein. This development has led to the fact that there are at the moment two diametrically opposed views. The students of cosmogony are divided into two camps, each of which has succeeded in bringing forward a variety of arguments substantiating the correctness of its own point of view, and rapping each other's knuckles, naturally in all friendliness, on discovering weak points in the 'opponent's' arguments. There are in fact innumerable weak points in the reasonings of both groups. In the final analysis the duration of man's existence, even if it is desired to put it at not less than a million years, is only a fraction of a second in the time-scale of the universe. Cosmogonists are like ephemera who are studying history. It need not therefore surprise us that cosmogony has so far, in spite of all the exact technical aids and mathematical niceties, not advanced farther than theories, objective proof of the correctness of which has still to be produced.

There are two groups of theories. One proceeds from the idea that the universe, as we partly know it, had a beginning, the other believes in the view that the matter which we perceive in the universe is of a temporary nature, but that the universe itself has always been and has always looked just as we perceive it.

That sounds rather obscure. We will try to state briefly the bases of the two views. Within the two groups there are, of course, differences of opinion between the adherents of both theories amongst themselves, but we will not become involved in these, because they are not important from our point of view.

The naturalized American and former Russian, Professor Dr. G. Gamow, professor of theoretical physics at the George Washington University, is one of the most eloquent spokesmen of the 'beginning group'; the English astronomer, F. Hoyle, is one of the most ardent advocates of the 'always group.' These two names will occur quite often. We shall not however be referring to these two persons as such, but to the two groups, each consisting of very authoritative figures, of whom we, in spite of their mutual differences of opinion and whether they approve of it or not, will allow Gamow and Hoyle to be the representatives.

Gamow bases his theory on the fact that the universe is expanding, a fact which has been confirmed by observations. The universe is expanding and can, therefore, not always have been as it is now, says Gamow. We see through telescopes that the milliards of galaxies in space are moving farther apart. If we could make time to run backwards, then we should see the systems approaching one another. The universe would become smaller and smaller, until all the matter and energy were collected at one point. Gamow considers that it must have begun in this way. Once, a very long time ago, there was a point where all the matter and energy which exist were packed together. That point was not somewhere in the universe, no, that point was the universe and outside it there was nothing, no space, no time, there was not even any 'beyond.' We cannot conceive of the form and dimensions of that point, for the universe is unlimited and always has been, even 'then.' We can certainly estimate the density and the temperature in the 'point universe.' The density must have been so enormous that 1 cubic centimetre would have weighed no less than 100 million metric tons according to terrestrial standards. The temperature must have amounted to milliards and milliards of degrees. In that heat everything must have existed in the form of nuclear gas, a gas of free primitive particles, such as protons, neutrons and electrons which were tossed to and fro by powerful quanta of energy.

Then the universe exploded. Why? This is Gamow's answer in his own words: 'The Great Packing Together which took place in primordial times was the result of a collapse which dated from an even earlier period, and the present expansion is simply an elastic rebound which occurred as soon as the maximum possible density had been achieved.'

Our universe must therefore, in Gamow's opinion, have been formed by the passing away of a former universe. The matter of the former universe was thrown together with such great force that all the atoms were broken down into their constituent particles, forming an extremely hot and dense 'nuclear gas.' The explosion took place, and the universe flew apart with force—the expansion had begun. The density decreased, the temperature fell. That gave the elementary particles the opportunity to group together once again as atoms. When the temperature and density had fallen only slightly, the atoms of the heaviest elements were the first to be formed. Gamow has calculated that for the formation of the uranium nucleus, for example, a pressure of millions of tons and a heat of milliards of degrees are necessary.

Is it not a strange idea that, if Gamow is correct, the nuclear energy, which we are at the moment liberating in reactors, was enclosed in the uranium nucleus at the time of the formation of the universe?

As the expansion progressed, the temperature and density became less and less, so that lighter and lighter elements were formed successively from the disorderly collection of nuclear particles. Finally the excess protons provided themselves with electrons, and hydrogen was formed as the last element.

The whole process of the formation of atoms according to Gamow cannot have lasted more than one hour. After that hour there was an expanding universe, consisting of one huge cloud of gas, containing all matter and energy and having a temperature of several hundred degrees. During the next 30 million years nothing in particular happened, Gamow states laconically. The cloud continued to expand and cool off. When the temperature and density were suitable, the cloud began to condense, nuclei were formed around which the gas contracted. The 'primordial cloud' dissolved into milliards of masses of gas and matter, which moved farther apart as a result of the expansion of the universe, these being the subsequent galaxies. Condensation also occurred in the separate masses of gas. The gas collected together around milliards of condensation nuclei, it began to contract under its own weight.

Up till then, after the hellish light of the first hour, it had been dark in the universe, for there was nothing that could give light. Yet, as the spheres of gas in the resultant galaxies contracted further, they became hotter and hotter, and at a certain moment a temperature was reached at which the nuclear fusion process in hydrogen proceeds of its own accord. The spheres of gas flared up, the first stars illuminated the young universe, floating in groups through expanding space.

And where were 'we' then?

The earth came into existence at about the same time as the sun, according to Gamow. Not all matter of the gaseous cloud which was to become our sun finished up in the body of the sun. Outside that body there was a formless mass of gas and matter, in which the atoms and molecules wandered about. In that mass there must have occurred, as a mathematical treatment of this subject has shown, a system of eddies and those eddies gave rise to local condensation, from which the general force of attraction gradually made planets. It was therefore not due to any exception or chance that the sun acquired a planetary system. According to Gamow, it is reasonable to suppose that stars, which were formed under similar conditions to our sun, have planets, and this applies to milliards of stars!

This refers to the 'how,' which is immediately followed by the question 'when'? Gamow has also given an answer to this, but it seems likely that the latest scientific advances will make it necessary to revise the answer. Gamow places the moment of the explosion at somewhere between 3 and 4 milliard years ago. We now however have indications that our earth, our sun and our galaxy are at least 5 milliard years old. There is even mention of 7 milliard years. Whether this much greater age can be brought into agreement with Gamow's explosion theory, remains to be seen. Hoyle is inclined to assume that it cannot.

Hoyle is, after all, in complete disagreement with Gamow all along the line. According to him, the universe did not come into existence at a given moment in the past, but is still in the course of coming into existence. At this moment, in Hoyle's view, creation is still going on, just as it always has been and always will be.

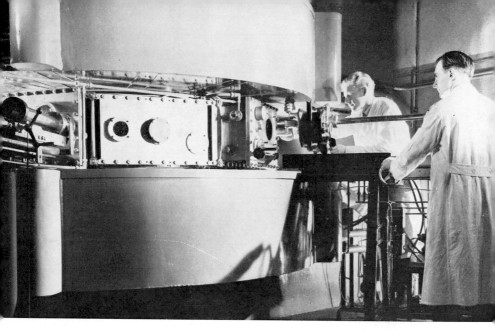

The cyclotron in Amsterdam, owned by N.V. Philips. Philips use the apparatus for the preparation of radioactive isotopes. It is also used by the Institute for Nuclear Physics Research.

The electron microscope and an enlargement made with it. The bacteria which cause yellow-spot disease in hyacinths are magnified 13,000 times.

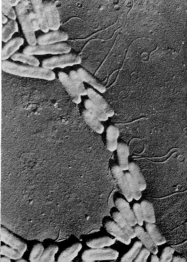

Prof. Werner Heisenberg, one of the world's outstanding scientists. At the age of 31, he was awarded the Nobel Prize for physics. He maintains that he has found the basic formula of all science, both of the microcosm and the macrocosm, and is now engaged in proving his theory. Will he have found what Einstein sought in vain throughout his whole life?

Fred Hoyle, whose theories about the origin of the universe have been widely discussed in recent years and who has achieved great popularity by his clearly written books about them.

In his theory the English astronomer does not take any account of what has so far been considered the correct view, namely that space is curved and returns upon itself. According to him, the universe is infinite, both in space and time. Hoyle needs no more than the three 'normal' dimensions, which we call length, breadth and height. Yet—and this sounds strange— Hoyle, in common with Gamow, assumes that the universe is expanding. And what is even stranger, he says that the universe has always been in its present state, in other words that it has always been expanding. And to go a step further, to an observer, wherever he may be in the universe, it has, according to Hoyle, always been just as large, in spite of the expansion.

Those who turn away from Hoyle with a shrug of the shoulders act reasonably, but are wrong, for after a little thought it is possible, even as a layman, to get some idea of Hoyle's picture of the universe. For this one need only realize what the scientist means by 'space,' and that is fairly simple. Space is nothing more than the distance between parts or particles of matter. If the distance between two objects becomes larger, then more space arises; if it becomes less, then space disappears. Let us imagine that the universe is quite empty, that there is no galaxy, no sun, no planet, no atom, no electron, no quantum of energy. There is but one speck of dust in it. Can we then speak of space? No, what would we have to measure that space in relation to? If a second speck of dust is involved, then there is at the same time space, for the distance between two particles of material, whether large or small, can be measured. There is space between them. That is then the position with all space in the whole of the universe!

Just as with Gamow, we will let time run backwards with Hoyle. We then see the universe shrink instead of expanding. We see all the milliards of galaxies racing towards one another, their distances apart become smaller and smaller—there will soon be a catastrophe! Yes, that is the case with Gamow's theory, but no accidents happen according to Hoyle's view.

Let us greatly simplify the matter and assume that we can go and stand at a place where we can see six galaxies approaching one another. Three of them approach from the left and three from the right, each one nicely behind the other, and consequently all six of them in a straight line. At the place where we are standing they will have to hit each other, just as cars hit one another in a collision: one from the left and one from the right touch, then comes another from the left and one from the right, and finally the last from the left and that from the right drift into the mess. But no, there are no collisions! Before the first from the left and the first from the right can touch one another, these groups of stars cease to exist! They dissolve into nothing! And what happens with the space? The space between the two gets smaller and smaller as time goes on and finally ceases to exist as well. After all, when the groups are no more, there is also no longer any distance or space between them.

There is also no longer any space between the first and the second on the right after the first has ceased to exist, that is clear. Is there then no longer any space in our simplified universe? Of course—just as much as there was before! For there is distance between number two from the left and number two from the right, which have in the meantime come to occupy the places where numbers one were before they ceased to exist. There is also space between numbers two and three on each side, in fact just as much as there originally was between numbers one and two. The development goes on. Numbers two as well cease to exist when they threaten to collide, the space between them disappears, but space remains to the same extent as it did before, for numbers three are still there.

We therefore see, as long as there are galaxies which approach one another, that space contracts without changing its character. If we consider not six, but an infinitely large number of groups of stars, coming not from two, but from innumerable directions, this does not alter the principle at all. We see space shrinking, without becoming smaller. How does this happen? It is due to the fact that matter ceases to exist. The universe can consequently shrink without changing and, if there are infinitely many systems of stars, without becoming smaller. This happens if matter ceases to exist and dissolves into nothing.

This is the opposite picture. We let the clock run in the opposite direction. The real picture, Hoyle's picture, now becomes much easier to understand. The universe is expanding and matter is being formed out of nothing, space is getting larger without changing its nature.

This is precisely the core of Hoyle's theory. The universe is still coming into existence, since new matter is being formed of its own accord in expanding space. There is even, according to Hoyle, a close scientific relationship between the speed of the expansion and the amount of material which is being formed. They are in precise equilibrium, so that the average density of the universe always remains the same. Every second about a quarter of a million hydrogen atoms are formed in a space equal to the volume of the earth or, as Hoyle remarks, about one atom per century in a volume equal to that of the Empire State Building in New York. This is, in the part of the universe which is visible to us, that is to say in a sphere with a radius of about 6 milliard light years, 10^{32} or 100 quintillion metric tons per second![1]

Hoyle considers that things have always been going on like this. There was never a beginning, for however many billion centuries one likes to go back, there was always, for the chosen period, a universe with space, matter and energy. The universe is consequently eternal and has always had the form which it still has. Only the matter in it is not eternal, for that came into existence of its own accord when the increase in the distance between the already existing matter made that necessary.

New matter, according to Hoyle, more or less follows the path suggested by Gamow. As soon as density and temperature determine it, condensation occurs. Contraction and consequent heating follow, new galaxies, new stars come into existence.

According to Hoyle, there takes place in the stars what according to Gamow took place in the primeval explosion, namely the building up of the sorts of atoms, the elements. The process of nuclear fusion in the stars makes helium from hydrogen as we know. But what happens if a star has virtually used up all its hydrogen? That depends, according to Hoyle, on its mass. The lighter examples—like our sun—die peacefully and calmly, after having passed through very complicated processes. The position is however different with the heavier stars. In them nature switches over to helium as a 'fuel' when there is a shortage of hydrogen, and constructs heavier elements

[1] It is clear that what was described in Chapter IX about the size and content of the curved universe is based on a different theory from that of Hoyle. In Hoyle's case there is naturally no question of the contents of the universe being a fixed magnitude. The views in Chapter IX are based on theories advocated by Gamow and his colleagues.

from it, likewise by nuclear fusion. When the helium is used up, the heavier elements which are then present are transformed into still heavier ones, and so on. Everything comes to an end, however—even the possibilities of fusion. The end is that the star bursts asunder with indescribable force.

We know that phenomenon. It is the supernova phenomenon which we have already considered. Milliards of tons of matter, consisting of all types of light and heavy elements, are forced into space by the star. The atoms then mix with the newly formed hydrogen, at least according to Hoyle. Old and new matter meet and form the clouds of gas and dust from which, after millions and millions of years, galaxies with suns and planets will be formed.

If we are to believe Hoyle our earth and *we* therefore consist of atoms which were once formed in the hot nucleus of stars and which spread into the universe during supernova explosions. There have always been suns and planets, for there have always been earlier supernovae which provided the heavier elements necessary for their construction. What a grandiose word 'always' is in this context!

By strictly logical reasoning, we could draw the conclusion from all this that an observer somewhere in the universe must, however, notice a difference between the present state and of that, let us say, 100 milliard years ago. After all, there is at present much more matter, and innumerable new galaxies have come into existence. Hoyle does not agree with this conclusion. He refers, once again, to the expansion of the universe. Observation has taught that the speed of expansion is directly proportional to the distance. The farther one galaxy is from us, the more quickly it moves with regard to us. Systems which lie 'very close' to us move at speeds of a few hundred kilometres per second, galaxies at a distance of 3 milliard light years or so move away at not less than 64,000 kilometres per second. Those fast systems lie at the limits of our present powers of perception. If we could see even farther, and then farther still, and so on, would we then come to a limiting speed?

Yes. We would come to a limit, namely to the limit where the speed of the systems of stars, relative to us, equals the maximum speed in nature, namely the speed of the propagation of light in empty space, that is 300,000 kilometres per second. Beyond that limit there is nothing more for us. For an observer, wherever he may be in the universe, nothing changes, in spite of the coming into existence of new matter, since at the same time 'old' matter has, relative to him, attained the speed of light, and has thereby ceased to exist for him!

There is some point here in stressing the relativity of nature. It was Einstein's conclusion that we cannot state anything absolutely. Everything has to be measured, determined, calculated *with reference to something else,* and it is clear that man measures, determines and calculates everything relative to the earth. Only what he can relate in some way to our planet is to him reality. The fact that an observer at quite a different place in the universe knows quite a different reality may give rise to playful fantasies, but has no scientific importance. Those things which are racing away from us at the speed of light do not exist for us. Scientifically, we may even say that they do not exist. This is the reason why Hoyle says that the universe has always been as it is now. Matter comes into existence and matter ceases to exist—the universe is eternal. Just as man is more than the collection of atoms from which he is built up, the universe is more than the whole of the matter and energy of which it exists.

This is consequently Hoyle's picture of the world. Generations of galaxies produce generations of galaxies, from eternity to eternity, in a rhythm which is now slower and now faster, but which always remains itself. A human generation is to us thirty years. We may, according to the data which Hoyle states he now has, place a galaxy generation at 7 milliard years!

And in one of those infinitely many generations the human race lives on its small planet, worrying about the question as to how long eternity lasts.

Who is right, Gamow or Hoyle? No one knows. Perhaps both of them are partly right, perhaps both are completely wrong. What we perceive is, in the final analysis, merely a shadow of the reality we shall never know.

Serious arguments can be brought forward against both theories. We will mention a few of the most important.

Gamow's theory is one of chance. There was an 'accident' with a universe, and the present universe owes its existence to this. If it could be shown that our universe, just as its predecessor, will one day collapse, and thereby a new creation come into existence, then Gamow's position would be very strong, because then there would be no question of a chance, but of a law of nature. For then we would have to assume that this is the eternal cycle of things, explosion, expansion, contraction, collapse, explosion, expansion, and so on—the universe would be like a beating heart. Nevertheless, according to present knowledge, that is not so. Mathematical treatment of the expansion has shown that the universe, as we know it, will always have to continue expanding and will never again be able to contract. The original explosion would therefore have been something which occurred once and can never be repeated, consequently a chance, caused by something or another. Nature does not however know chance, it knows only laws. Unless science comes to the conclusion that its estimates may be incorrect and a future contraction of the universe is, after all, considered possible, it consequently looks bad for Gamow's theory.

The score is 1–0 in favour of Hoyle! He proceeds from the assumption that the universe is eternally expanding. But in all fairness we will straight away make the score 1 all, for Hoyle's theory fails as well, namely in the construction of the heavy elements. If Hoyle were right, then the heaviest elements could not occur in nature. Gamow has calculated that for the formation of the uranium nucleus a pressure of millions of tons and a temperature of milliards of degrees are necessary. That pressure and temperature are not reached in any type of star known to us. Mathematical considerations of the supernova phenomenon lead to the conclusion that, even at that inconceivable force, the physical circumstances do not exist which are necessary for the formation of the heaviest elements. Another objection to Hoyle's theory is that the distribution of matter over the different elements would have to be quite different.

We will not consider further the extremely complicated points connected with all this, and will leave the score in the match between Gamow and Hoyle as one all, and leave it to the future to decide who is the winner—assuming there will be a winner.

Let us return from the depths of the cosmos to our planet and our sun. Interesting as the question of the past of the universe is, the future is more important to man.

What will happen to our solar system? What will be the fate of the sun in the near or distant future? We have already touched on the extremely slight chance that our star will explode. Let us not consider that further, but see for a moment what the probable normal development will be.

The age of the sun is estimated at the moment at about 5 milliard years. 5,000 million years ago the sun condensed out of gas and dust to form the immense glowing ball we know. It is still young, for the most recent estimates say that it can easily reach the age of forty, that is 40 milliard years. Will our descendants 'in due course' see its decline? Will man disappear at the same time as the sun?

No human eye will see the sun die.

In the first place biological evolution is a reason why no single form of life can maintain itself for an unlimited period. Just as once the giant reptiles disappeared, man will one day disappear as a species. Perhaps he will get the worst of it against the legions of insects which have already begun their advance and are now presenting man with very great problems. The duration of a form of life can only be expressed in millions of years, and in the cosmos we have to reckon with milliards. But in the second place, even if man were to be an exception and succeed in maintaining himself biologically, he would still not live to see the disappearance of the sun. The sun will start using up its hydrogen all the more quickly the faster its supply subsides. It will gradually get warmer, radiating more heat and light. Since organic life on earth is possible only between quite narrow limits of temperature, it will die out with the steady increase in temperature. Life is not possible if the oceans boil and vaporize and metals melt. The highest organized creature with the lowest possibilities of adaption, namely man, will be the first victim. Finally, even the strongest bacteria and viruses will succumb. Then the earth will again be just as desolate and empty as it was for milliards of years, and will again be for milliards of years. Life on this planet is merely a very short intermezzo in its existence, too short to be expressed on the clock of the universe, even in thousandths of seconds. Without a terrestrial eye seeing it, the sun will gradually swell as it becomes hotter and reaches the climax of its lustre and glow. Once it has given its maximum powers, it will collapse, shrink like an old man, become extinguished like a cinder which continues to glow in the fire. Then it will be dark for ever. Then our solar system will have become a collection of dead matter, for which time and eternity have become the same. It will cease to exist as regards life elsewhere in the universe, if it has ever existed for it.

Long before the sun sets man will have died out. How long can he still continue to exist? For a further 10 milliard years according to a rough estimate, if he succeeds in maintaining himself biologically. Only after 10,000 million years will life here have become impossible, as far as the sun is concerned.

Man will be able to continue to exist for a further 10 milliard years, living between the two worlds which intrigue him, between the macrocosm and the microcosm, between what is large and what is small. What a unique chance he has!

We shall live a long time! 10 milliard years—providing we are sensible.

CHAPTER XVI

MAN'S PLACE BETWEEN STARS AND ATOMS

Our journey is at an end. For fifteen chapters we have wandered about through the infinities of the macrocosm and the depths of the microcosm. We have seen what it is like on Jupiter and what it is like in a nuclear reactor. We have seen the universe expanding, and the electron circling around the nucleus of the atom. We have paused at the wonderful unity of time and space and at the use of radioactive isotopes. We have given a bird's eye view of virtually all that fascinating and colourful world which goes under the name of modern science.

We have tried to say objectively what that science knows, assumes or supposes. What the author himself thinks of all sorts of theories and suppositions he has kept to himself, not considering them as important here. It was a question of making clear to the reader what the general modern picture of the world looks like, and not of how the author interprets it.

Now however, at the parting of the ways, we must have a short subjective chapter. The reader now possesses the objective data which he needs to form a personal opinion. The author now wishes to add something to this, feeling that it can contribute to a correct appreciation of the facts. He would like, in fact, to issue a serious warning against an over-estimation of the value and importance of science.

That warning is already concealed in the title of the book. Man's place is 'between stars and atoms.' In other words, man is the central figure. In the stormy scientific development of the last twenty years man has threatened to move more and more into the background. Science and technical matters have started to lead their own, independent lives, in which man has been left less and less space as time has gone on. At least that is how it seems.

But it is definitely not so. Man is the central figure and will always remain so. Science and techniques proceed from man and their development is dependent on him.

Man is the determining factor in knowledge, and in science as well. The fact that Jupiter exists owes its importance solely to the circumstance that there lives on earth a being who observes it.

We must not, therefore, think of the value and importance of the various branches of science as being absolute. They are very, very large and will become much larger, of course, but they are relative. Knowledge has proved that again and again. What was yesterday an irresponsible modernism will tomorrow be a confirmed point of view.

In considering and evaluating the scientific picture of the world, we must, above all, bear in mind that this picture is a silhouette, as we explained in Chapter XIV, a shadow of reality.

We can analyse Mozart's Jupiter Symphony scientifically, can disentangle it according to the strict rules of composition and explain it in a substantial document, supported by reasons why Mozart has used certain chords and intervals. Then we shall have drawn a scientific picture of the symphony, a reliable picture, but nothing more than a silhouette. The real symphony is that harmonic flow of sounds, of instrumental timbres, of tensions and resolutions which cause the listener in the concert-hall to feel the experience of beauty, the emotion of sublime harmony. That experience, that emotion is the real picture of the Jupiter Symphony and that picture can never be reproduced by science in its objective formulae. This essence eludes it.

The essential features cannot be formulated. There is no formula which can express love, uncertainty, jealousy, repentance, longing, belief. No science in the world can analyse why one person finds the songs of Doris Day pleasant, and the other likes sprouts and does not like swedes, to give a few trivial examples. The nature of things escapes science.

For this reason science can never be regarded as the only important thing which determines everything, for the main point is the nature of things, their essential nature. That nature differs for every human being. That essential feature is a mystery for everyone, but each person gives that mystery a name. One speaks of God, the other of Nature, the third of Fate, the fourth of Primordial Force. This is the sacred region of the deepest personal conviction.

Science is powerless when confronted by this mystery. Its field is that of numbers, formulae, exact descriptions. This mystery cannot be captured by these. Man must therefore again and again put science in its place, if it tries to master him. Man may serve science, like it, honour it, but he must in all cases remain its master. If he does not, then he lowers himself to the level of his own silhouette, to a number, a collection of atoms, a factor in a formula, which are soulless because they lack the essential factor. In view of developments during the last few decades, in which science has been rolling on like a powerful steam-roller, the author considers it necessary to add this warning to his book.

He also has a second reason for this. Here and there the reader may have gained the impression that the writer considers man as insignificant in the cosmos as a whole. The writer no longer needs to say that this impression is incorrect. Man is, in the totality of things, the most important element—for man.

If he constantly realizes this when judging—and possibly condemning—what has been offered in this book, then the author will be satisfied.

APPENDIX

I. THE EARTH AND THE MOON

	Earth	*Moon*
Average distance apart	149½ million km. from the sun	385,000 km. from the earth
Orbital speed ..	29·8 km./sec. on an average	1·017 km./sec. on an average
Period of orbital revolution	365 d. 5 h. 48 m. 46 s.	27 d. 7 h. 43 m. 11½ s.
Period of axial rotation	23 h. 56 m. 4·09 s.	27 d. 7 h. 43 m. 11½ s.
Diameter ..	12,757 km.	3,480 km.
Circumference	40,076 km.	10,937 km.
Area	510 million km.^{2}	38 million km.^{2}
Volume ..	1,083 milliard km.^{3}	22 milliard km.^{3}
Mass * ..	6×10^{24} kg.†	$7·3 \times 10^{22}$ kg.
Density‡ ..	5·53	3·37

* Mass is the amount of matter in a body and is expressed in terrestrial kilogrammes. Mass is not, however, equivalent to weight. Mass is the same everywhere, while weight varies from place to place.

† In science, it is the custom to write large numbers as powers of 10, which greatly facilitates working. 6×10^{24} is much more easy to handle than 6,000,000,000,000,000,000,000,000.

‡ Density corresponds to the term specific gravity, consequently it is the number which indicates how many times one cubic centimetre of a substance is heavier than one cubic centimetre of pure water at 4° C.

II. THE PLANETARY SYSTEM

	Mercury	Venus	Earth	Mars	Jupiter	Saturn	Uranus	Neptune	Pluto
Average distance from the sun in million km.	58	108	149·5	228	778	1,420	2,870	4,490	5,900
Period of orbital revolution	88 d.	225 d.	1 y.	1·9 y.	11·9 y.	29·5 y.	84 y.	165 y.	248 y.
Orbital speed in km./sec.	48	35	29·8	24	13	10	6·8	5·4	4·7
Period of axial rotation	88 d.	?	23 h. 56 m. 4·09 s.	24 h. 37 m. 23 s.	9 h. 50 m.	10 h. 14 m.	10 h. 45 m.	15 h. 40 m.	?
Diameter in km.	5,000	12,400	12,757	6,800	140,000	116,000	50,000	53,000	6,000 (?)
Mass (earth=1)	0·04	0·82	1	0·11	318	95	15	17	0·1 (?)
Volume (earth=1)	0·06	0·92	1	0·15	1,310	760	59	72	1 (?)
Average density	3·9	4·9	5·53	3·9	1·3	0·7	1·3	1·3	?
Gravitational force at surface (earth=1)	0·27	0·85	1	0·38	2·64	1·17	0·92	1·12	?
Mean surface temperature in °C.	330 (at side facing the sun)	57 (?)	15	−15	−130	−150	lower than −185	lower than −185	?
Number of moons	0	0	1	2	12	9	5	1	?

158

III. TOTAL SOLAR ECLIPSES BETWEEN 1962 AND 2000

Year	Date	Course of Region of Totality
1962	5/2	Borneo, New Guinea, central and northern Pacific.
1963	20/7	Japan, Bering Sea, Alaska, northern Canada, central part of north Atlantic.
1965	30/5	South Pacific, New Zealand, Marquesas Islands, Peru.
1966	20/5	Atlantic Ocean, north-west Africa, Mediterranean, straight across Asia.
1966	12/11	Pacific, west of Galapagos Islands, straight across southern South America, over Atlantic to Indian Ocean.
1967	2/11	Antarctic Ocean, south polar region.
1968	22/9	Arctic Ocean, north Russia to central Asia.
1970	7/3	Central Pacific, Mexico, Florida to central northern Atlantic.
1972	10/7	North-east Asia, Alaska, northern Canada to central Atlantic Ocean.
1973	30/6	Northern South America, Atlantic Ocean, over north Africa to central Indian Ocean.
1974	20/6	Southern Indian Ocean and Antarctic, south of Australia.
1976	23/10	East Africa, over Indian Ocean and Australia to point near New Zealand.
1977	12/10	Central northern Pacific, south-west to northern South America.
1979	26/2	Northern Pacific, north-west point of United States over Canada and Hudson Bay to central Greenland.
1980	16/2	Atlantic Ocean, over central Africa, Indian Ocean, India, southern China.
1981	31/7	South-east Europe, over Siberia to central northern Pacific.
1983	11/6	Southern Indian Ocean, over Indonesia to western Pacific.
1984	30/5	Pacific, Mexico, southern United States, Atlantic Ocean to north Africa.
1984	22/11	Indonesia, over southern Pacific to point just off coast of Chile.
1985	12/11	Antarctic Ocean.
1986	3/10	Atlantic Ocean, from south-west coast of Greenland.
1987	29/3	Patagonia, southern Atlantic, right across Africa.

Year	Date	Course of Region of Totality
1988	18/3	Eastern Indian Ocean, over Sumatra, Malacca, northern Pacific, Philippines, to point south of Alaska.
1990	22/7	Finland, Arctic Ocean, north-east Asia, straight across northern Pacific.
1991	11/7	Central Pacific, over Mexico, central America, northern South America to Brazil.
1992	30/6	South-east South America, over centre of southern Atlantic Ocean to border of Indian Ocean and Antarctic.
1994	3/11	Pacific south of Galapagos Islands over South America and southern Atlantic to west part of Indian Ocean.
1995	24/10	South-west Asia, north India, Malacca, to central Pacific.
1997	9/3	Central Asia, north-east Asia to Arctic Ocean.
1998	26/2	Central Pacific, over extreme north of South America, Atlantic Ocean to Canary Islands.
1999	11/8	Atlantic Ocean south of Nova Scotia, over north Atlantic, central Europe, southern Asia to north India.

IV. A RETURN JOURNEY TO SIRIUS AND ITS CONSEQUENCES

Let us assume that it is technically possible for us to build a space-ship which can reach a speed equal to 99% of that of light in an empty space, this latter being, for the sake of convenience, 300,000 km./sec. The latest measurements give a value of 299,776 km./sec. The difference of less than $\frac{1}{2}$% will not affect our calculations to any great extent. Our space-ship can, therefore, reach a speed of $99 \times 3,000 = 297,000$ km./sec.

A man leaves for a planet of the star Sirius in this ship. We are of course assuming, for the sake of convenience, that this star has a planet. The distance between the earth and the planet of Sirius is $8 \cdot 8$ light years. The traveller makes the journey there and back and will therefore cover $2 \times 8 \cdot 8$ light years $= 164 \times 10^{12}$ km.

There is no difficulty whatsoever for those who have remained behind on the earth in calculating the time of return. The traveller will, providing he turns round immediately on reaching the planet of Sirius, return after $164 \times 10^{12} \div 297,000 = 558,929,292$ seconds, in other words, after 17 years and 180 days.

Now the theory of relativity teaches us that objects which move at a certain speed relative to us have a time which passes more slowly than our own. One of the so-called transformation formulae, borrowed by Einstein from the work of the Dutchman, Dr. H. A. Lorentz, enables us to calculate the ratio between the two times, providing the relative speed is known. This formula is:

$$t_1 = \frac{t_0}{\sqrt{1 - v^2/c^2}}$$

where t_1 is the time of the moving object, t_0 is terrestrial time, v is the relative speed and c is the speed of light in empty space.

In our case, this becomes:

$$t_1 = t_0 \div \sqrt{1 - 297,000^2/300,000^2}$$

or $\quad t_1 = t_0 \div \sqrt{1 - 0 \cdot 9801} = t_0 \div \sqrt{0 \cdot 0199} = t_0 \div 0 \cdot 141 \ldots$

Consequently $t_1 = t_0 \div \frac{1}{7}$, or $\frac{1}{7} t_1 = t_0$, which means that the time of the astronaut is seven times terrestrial time. In other words, 1 second in the space-ship has a value of 7 terrestrial seconds. On his return to the earth a seventh of the number of seconds will have passed for the astronaut compared with the number of seconds which have passed on earth since his departure. He thinks, therefore, that he has been away for $558,929,292 \div 7 = 79,847,041$ seconds or 2 years and 194 days. And not only does he think it—he *has not* been away for a longer period, he is only 2 years and 194 days older. His watch was not losing, time itself passed more slowly, so that he breathed more slowly, thought more slowly, lived more slowly, became older more slowly than those who remained behind on the earth. He did not notice anything of this himself—for him a second was a second, both on the earth and later in his space-ship.

It could be concluded on earth from this that the traveller had experienced something strange with his speed, which was, for us, 297,000 km./sec. He was away for 2 years and 194 days, but nevertheless covered 164×10^{12} km. Since his time passed more slowly, his speed must have become faster. He must have travelled at a speed of $164 \times 10^{12} = 79,847,041 =$ about 2 million km./sec., which is more than six times the speed of light!

This is however at variance with the laws of nature, which say that the speed of light is the maximum possible speed. From whatever moving system we start, greater speeds than this are physically impossible.

This reasoning is also incorrect, although it is unfortunately found more and more at the moment in books and magazines. For, apart from a slowing down of time, there is also a shortening of length in the direction of movement. In other words, all dimensions of an object become shorter in the direction in which the object is moving. This too is a relative shortening; the traveller himself will not notice it at all. He can show in a completely correct physical manner that the shortening does not occur with him, but that it is precisely the line from the earth to the planet of Sirius, along which he is travelling, which has become shorter, since that line is moving past him at a high speed. In the same way he can equally correctly say that no slowing down of time occurs with him, but that this happens on earth, since the earth is moving relative to him!

The distance to be covered was therefore different for the traveller from that measured on the earth. The length can be calculated by another transformation formula:

$$l_1 = l_0 \sqrt{1 - v^2/c^2}$$

in which l_1 is the distance for the traveller and l_0 that for the earth. If we use this formula, then we obtain:

$$l_1 = l_0 \times 0 \cdot 141 \ldots = 0 \cdot 14 \times 164 \times 10^{12} = 23 \text{ billion km.}$$

What is 164 billion km. for those on the earth is 23 billion km. for the traveller. He has in 8×10^7 (simplification of 79,847,041) seconds covered 23×10^{12} km. That is $23 \times 10^{12} \div 8 \times 10^7 =$ about 290,000 km./sec. Since we have used simplifications for the sake of convenience in our calculation, this value is somewhat too low. We do not really need this calculation, since in both formulae $\sqrt{1-v^2/c^2}$ gives the same result, in other words time and distance are influenced by the same factor, so that their mutual ratio remains unchanged, and consequently the speed does not alter.

The astronaut has in his special moving system therefore travelled at 99% of the speed of light—he has not exceeded the maximum speed in the universe at any time.

In view of the relative character of space and time, we can establish precisely the same calculations from the point of view of the astronaut. The figures then show that time on the earth has passed seven times as slowly as in the space-ship. Then we begin to wonder what is the truth. The consequences of these calculations have been discussed in detail in Chapter VIII. These possibilities were given there, each of which finds adherents amongst scholars. Applied to our example, these three possible consequences—only one of which will possibly one day turn out in practice to be correct—are:

Possibility 1: earth 17 years and 180 days older, astronaut 2 years and 194 days older.

Possibility 2: earth and astronaut 17 years and 180 days older.

Possibility 3: earth and astronaut 2 years and 194 days older.

V. LIST OF NATURAL AND ARTIFICIAL ELEMENTS

1. Hydrogen (H)
2. Helium (He)
3. Lithium (Li)
4. Beryllium (Be)
5. Boron (B)
6. Carbon (C)
7. Nitrogen (N)
8. Oxygen (O)
9. Fluorine (F)
10. Neon (Ne)
11. Sodium (Na)
12. Magnesium (Mg)
13. Aluminium (Al)
14. Silicon (Si)
15. Phosphorus (P)
16. Sulphur (S)
17. Chlorine (Cl)
18. Argon (A)
19. Potassium (K)
20. Calcium (Ca)
21. Scandium (Sc)
22. Titanium (Ti)
23. Vanadium (V)
24. Chromium (Cr)
25. Manganese (Mn)
26. Iron (Fe)
27. Cobalt (Co)
28. Nickel (Ni)
29. Copper (Cu)
30. Zinc (Zn)
31. Gallium (Ga)
32. Germanium (Ge)
33. Arsenic (As)
34. Selenium (Se)
35. Bromine (Br)
36. Krypton (Kr)
37. Rubidium (Rb)
38. Strontium (Sr)
39. Yttrium (Y)
40. Zirconium (Zr)
41. Niobium (Nb)
42. Molybdenum (Mo)
43. Technetium (Tc)
44. Ruthenium (Ru)
45. Rhodium (Rh)
46. Palladium (Pd)
47. Silver (Ag)
48. Cadmium (Cd)
49. Indium (In)
50. Tin (Sn)
51. Antimony (Sb)
52. Tellurium (Te)
53. Iodine (J)
54. Xenon (Xe)
55. Caesium (Cs)
56. Barium (Ba)
57. Lanthanium (La)
58. Cerium (Ce)
59. Praseodymium (Pr)
60. Neodymium (Nd)
61. Promethium (Pm)
62. Samarium (Sm)
63. Europium (Eu)
64. Gadolinium (Gd)
65. Terbium (Tb)
66. Dysprosium (Dy)
67. Holmium (Ho)
68. Erbium (Er)
69. Thulium (Tm)
70. Ytterbium (Yb)
71. Lutetium (Lu)
72. Hafnium (Hf)
73. Tantalum (Ta)
74. Tungsten (W)
75. Rhenium (Re)
76. Osmium (Os)
77. Iridium (Ir)
78. Platinum (Pt)
79. Gold (Au)
80. Mercury (Hg)
81. Thallium (Tl)
82. Lead (Pb)

83. Bismuth (Bi)	93. *Neptunium* (Np)
84. Polonium (Po)	94. *Plutonium* (Pu)
85. Astatine (At)	95. *Americium* (Am)
86. Radon (Rn)	96. *Curium* (Cm)
87. Francium (Fr)	97. *Berkelium* (Bk)
88. Radium (Ra)	98. *Californium* (Cf)
89. Actinium (Ac)	99. *Einsteinium* (Es)
90. Thorium (Th)	100. *Fermium* (Fm)
91. Protactinium (Pa)	101. *Mendelevium* (Md)
92. Uranium (U)	102. *Nobelium* (No)

The last ten elements, printed in italics, do not occur in nature. They have been made by man in the laboratory.

VI. $E = mc^2$

In the formula $E = mc^2$, E is expressed in ergs, m in grammes and c in cm./sec.

If we could completely transform 1 gramme of matter into energy, we would have $1 \times 30,000,000,000 \times 30,000,000,000 = 9 \times 10^{20}$ ergs.

Now 10^7 ergs $= 1$ joule $= 0 \cdot 239$ calorie.

We would therefore obtain from 1 gramme of matter $9 \times 10^{13} \times 0 \cdot 239$ cal $= 9 \times 239 \times 10^7$ kilogramme-calories $= 2,151 \times 10^7$ kcal, or approximately 2×10^{10} kcal.

In order to heat 1 kilogramme of water ($= 1$ litre of water) from $0°$ C. to $100°$ C., 100 kcal are needed. With 2×10^{10} kcal we can consequently heat 2×10^8 kg. water from 0 to $100°$ C., that is 2×10^5 or 200,000 metric tons.

ACKNOWLEDGEMENTS

Thanks are due to the following for permission to reproduce photographs:

United Press International: Albert Einstein; total solar eclipse, June 1954; Arend-Roland comet; origin of galaxies; space-travel fantasy; Dr. Krafft Ehricke; atomic bomb explosion; loading a nuclear reactor; 'Jeep' reactor; 'Hot space'; the 'Nautilus.'

United States Information Service: How a solar eclipse occurs; Mount Palomar Observatory; E. P. Hubble; Prof. G. van Biesbroek; recording solar eruptions; Dr. Wernher von Braun; Vanguard satellite.

Mount Wilson and Palomar Observatories: Solar flame; sun's corona; discovery of planet Pluto; Halley's comet; Milky Way; Hale telescope; spectrum of a star; Andromeda nebula.

United Kingdom Information Service: Jodrell Bank.

United Kingdom Atomic Energy Authority: Fast fission breeder, Dounreay.

U.S.S.R. Information Service: Other side of the moon.

Philips' Persbureau: Manufacture of radioactive isotopes; Amsterdam cyclotron; electron microscope; magnification of bacteria.

ANP photo: Nuclear physics laboratory at Gronigen; Panic in Putten.

Public Information Office, CERN: CERN research centre.

H. Kleibrink, Leyden: Prof. J. H. Oort.